5000 词床头灯英语学习读本

Holmes Stories

福尔摩斯探案集

原著　Arthur Conan Doyle
　　　[英] 亚瑟·柯南·道尔
改编　Kenneth Grahame
审订　Anna K. Lovett
注释　毛荣贵　王雪梅　朱　琳

航空工业出版社
北　京

图书在版编目（CIP）数据

福尔摩斯探案集：英文/王若平等主编. —北京：航空
工业出版社，2006.11（2011.1 重印）
（床头灯英语学习读本. 5000 词）
ISBN 978-7-80183-882-7

Ⅰ.①福… Ⅱ.①王… Ⅲ. ①英语—语言读物②侦探
小说—作品集—英国—现代 Ⅳ.① H319.4：I

中国版本图书馆 CIP 数据核字（2010）第 232192 号

床头灯英语学习读本 福尔摩斯探案集
Chuangtoudeng Yingyu Xuexi Duben Fuermosi Tanan Ji

航空工业出版社出版发行
（北京市安定门外小关东里 14 号　100029）
发行部电话:010-64815615　010-64978486

北京富生印刷厂印刷　　　　　全国各地新华书店经销
2006 年 11 月第 1 版　　　　　2011 年 1 月第 5 次印刷
开本:850×1168　　1/32　　印张:8.25　　字数:240 千字
印数:30001—35000　　　　　　　　定价:14.80 元

本社图书如有缺页、倒页、脱页、残页等情况，请与本社发行部联系负责
调换。对本书任何形式的侵权均由李文律师代理。电话:13601002700

《床头灯英语学习读本》
丛书学术委员会

前　言

◆ 英语是语言的帝国

　　全球 60 亿人中,有 3.8 亿人的母语是英语,2.5 亿人的第二母语是英语,12.3 亿人学习英语,33.6 亿人和英语有关。全世界电视节目的 75%、电子邮件的 80%、网络的 85%、软件源代码的 100% 都使用英语。40~50 年后,全球将有 50% 的人精通英语。全球约有 6000 种语言,21 世纪末其中的 90% 将消亡。届时英语作为主导语言的地位将进一步得到提升。

　　目前中国大约有 4 亿人在学英语,超过英国和美国的人口总和,这是中国努力与时代接轨、与国际接轨的一个重要标志,大量中国人熟练掌握国际通用语言是中华民族走向繁荣富强的必要保障。

◆ 全民学英语运动

　　中国近 20 年来兴起了一场轰轰烈烈的全民学英语的运动。其规模之大,范围之广,古今中外前所未有。

　　学生、教师、公务员、公司职员、商店店员、出租车司机等,各行各业,都在学英语。其学习过程的漫长,也令人感叹。从幼儿园、小学、中学、大学、硕士、博士,到毕业工作,出国,直至退休,一直都在学,英语的学习可谓是终生性的。

◆ 英语学了多年之后的尴尬

　　中国人学了多年英语之后,如果冷静地反省一下多年努力的成效,不难发现自己的英语水平令人十分尴尬。这里将具体表现列举一二。

● 读任何原版的英语杂志,如 Times(时代)、Newsweek(新闻周刊)、The Economists(经济学家),或者原版小说,如 Jane Eyre(简·爱)、

Gone with the Wind（飘）等，必须借助词典，因为我们随时都可能读不懂。即便查阅大部头的词典，我们常常还是不能理解文意，将文意理解得面目全非。最为可悲的是我们中很多人已经屈从于这种一知半解的阅读状态，甚至有人还荒唐地认为英语本身就是一门模模糊糊的语言，这样当然就更谈不上尝到读原汁原味英语的乐趣了。

● 学习和探索专业知识的主流载体仍然是汉语。但我们必须清楚：整个现代科学体系基本是用英语来描述和表达的，译成汉语会有一定程度的失真，而且必然导致滞后。

● 英语表达是一个更大的问题。主要体现在用英语写作以及用英语深入交谈上。事实上，大多数人只能用简单的英语来进行粗略的表述，无法顺利地参加国际学术会议或者进行国际贸易谈判。即便是学术水平很高的专家，在国际刊物上发表论文时，只能请仅懂英语不懂专业的人翻译。一篇在很多老外眼中不伦不类的论文就这样产生了。客观地讲，即使采用不太高的标准来衡量，在中国英语学习的失败率也应该在99％以上。

◆ 来自西方的教育理念

中国人读英语有个缺点，学习缺乏渐进性。他们习惯于读满篇都是生词的文章，以为这样"收获"才最大。结果他们的阅读不断地被查词典打断，一小时只能看两三页，读起来自然索然无味，最后只能作罢。这是中国人学英语的通病！读的文章几乎全部达到了语言学家所说的"frustration level"（使学生感到沮丧的程度）。

西方的语言学家和心理学家对英语学习者的阅读状况进行了大量的研究，结论令人非常吃惊：最适宜阅读的难度比我们长期所处的、我们所习惯的、我们头脑中定位的难度要低得多！只有文中生词量小到足以保证阅读的持续性时，语言吸收的效果才最好，语言水平的提高也最快。举个形象的例子：上山是从峭壁直接艰难攀登还是走平缓的盘山路好？显然，能够从峭壁登顶者寥寥无几！即使其能勉强成功，也远远落后于沿坦途行进者。

◆ 犹太民族的启示

曾经有人说：全世界的金钱装在美国人的口袋里，而美国人的金钱却装在犹太人的脑袋里。据统计，犹太人占世界总人口约 0.3%，却掌握着世界经济命脉。在全世界最富有的企业家中，犹太人占 50% 以上。无论是过去和现在，在知名的经济巨头中犹太人占有绝对的比例。如第一个亿万巨富、石油大王洛克菲勒，"美国股神"巴菲特，华尔街的缔造者摩根，花旗集团董事长威尔，"打开个人计算机直销大门"的戴尔，坐在全球软件头把交椅"甲骨文公司"的艾利森，华纳电影公司创办人华纳，电影世界的领头羊斯皮尔伯格，他们都是犹太人。

犹太人成就的背后就是他们的噬书习惯。联合国教科文组织调查表明，全世界读书最多的民族是犹太民族。其中以色列在人均拥有图书和出版社以及每年人均读书的比例上，超过了世界上任何一个国家，成为世界之最，平均每人每年读书 64 本。与之反差很大的是中华民族，平均每人每年读书 0.7 本。这之中有阅读习惯的中国人虽占 5%，却掌握着中国 80% 的财富。一句话，阅读，特别是经典名著的阅读，是一个人和民族崛起的最根本方法。

阅读不能改变人生的起点，但它可以改变人生的终点。不论出身高贵与卑贱，阅读都能改变人生的坐标和轨迹。

◆ 通往英语自由境界的阶梯

英语的自由境界指的是用英语自由地学习和工作；自由地阅读英文原版书刊和资料；自如地用英语表达和交流；自然地用英语进行思维；自主地用英语撰写论文和著作。

一个英语达到自由境界的人，他的生活也常常是令人羡慕的。清晨随手拿起一份国外的报纸或者杂志，一边喝着浓浓的咖啡，一边轻松、惬意地阅读。可以用英语自由地进行实质性的交谈和撰写书面材料。能够自由地在英文网页上荡漾，能够随时了解国外的最新科技动态或最新的商贸行情。自己的生存空间不再受到国界的限制，无论是交友、择偶，还是发展自己的事业，都有更宽的、跨国度的选择。

有一定英语基础的读者要想"修成正果"，达到英语的自由境界，最缺少的就是可读之书。市面上的英语读物粗粗看来似乎琳琅满目，但稍一细读就会发现这些语料要么是难度过低，词汇量只有一、两千词的相当于中学水平的简写本；要么是令人望而生畏、读之更是倍受挫折的原著，语料难度脱节甚至是"代沟"，严重地阻碍了英语中高级学习者对英语的掌握。床头灯英语5000词系列填补了这方面的空白，为读者打造了到达英语自由境界的阶梯。

◆ **本套读物的特色——真正适合中高级英语学习者的原汁原味英语读物**

● **难度适中**：本套读物用英语中核心5000词写成，对于难以理解之处均有注释，使你躺在床上不用翻词典就能顺利地读下去，在不知不觉中走向英语自由境界。

● **语言地道**：美国作家执笔，用流畅的现代英语写成，并保留了原著的语言特色。

● **选材经典**：皆为一生中不可不读的作品，读之可提高英语水平、积淀西方文化和提高人生境界。

● **情节曲折**：让你徜徉在一个又一个迥异奇妙的书中世界。

　　……

◆ **"床头灯"英语系列读物的使用方法：**

● 整个床头灯系列包含儿童、中学生、3000词、5000词、6500词等不同层次。你可以选择不用查字典你就能保证阅读的持续性的级别进入，这个级别最少读30本，体会一下用英语读懂名著的感

4

觉——英语形成语感、自信心增强。然后乘胜追击,读下一个级别的,每个级别读 30 本以上。

● 使用床头灯英语学习读本(英汉对照版)练写作:看书中汉语部分,然后你试着翻译成英文,再把你翻译的英文与书上的英文对比。

本套读物是通向英语自由王国的钥匙,是通往英语最高境界的签证。在中国走向世界的道路上,英语水平决定工资水平!让每天阅读半小时"床头灯"成为你生活中的一部分。我相信这才是英语成功的真谛。

与股神巴菲特吃一顿午餐要花几百万美金,这使人们注意到了与名人交流的昂贵。而与比巴菲特更著名的大家近距离沟通,只需要去读"床头灯"。

王若平　于北京

本系列丛书学习指导咨询中心:

北京汉英达外语信息咨询中心

地　址:北京市海淀区中关村东路华清商务会馆 1501 室

邮　编:100083

电　话:010 – 82867079

网　址:http://www.yinghanda.com

E-mail:wrx1@vip.sina.com

床头灯英语的 BLOG:http://chuangtoudeng.blog.sohu.com

人物关系表

本书中出现的主要人物：

Sherlock Holmes 夏洛克·福尔摩斯：著名私家侦探。

Dr. Watson 华生：医生，夏洛克·福尔摩斯最亲密的朋友和助手。

Lestrade 雷斯垂德：伦敦苏格兰场警探。

Mycroft Holmes 迈克罗夫特·福尔摩斯：夏洛克·福尔摩斯的哥哥。

Mrs. Hudson 哈德森太太：夏洛克·福尔摩斯的女仆。

本书十个故事中所涉及的主要反面人物：

《六座拿破仑半身像》

Beppo 倍波：工人，案件的罪犯。

《吸血鬼》

Jack 杰克：用毒箭扎伤弟弟的十五岁男孩。

《博斯科姆比溪谷秘案》

Charles McCarthy 查尔斯·麦卡锡：农场主，谋杀案的凶手。

《跳舞的人》

Abe Slaney 阿贝·斯兰尼：杀害希尔顿·丘比特先生的凶手。

《蓝宝石案》

James Ryder 詹姆斯·赖德：偷蓝宝石的旅馆领班。

《第二块血迹》

Lady Hilda Trelawney Hope 希尔达·崔洛尼·候普夫人：藏匿国家机密信件的大臣夫人。

《米尔沃顿案》

Charles Augustus Milverton 查尔斯·奥古斯塔斯·米尔沃顿：专靠收买别人的隐私信件而敲诈写信人的恶棍。

《空屋案》

Colonel Moran 莫兰上校：杀害罗纳德·阿德尔的凶手，也是企图谋害福尔摩斯的罪犯之一。

《工程师大拇指案》

Colonel Lysander Stark 莱桑德·斯塔克上校：伪造货币的主犯。

《肖斯科姆别墅》

Sir Robert 罗伯特爵士：为了赢得赛马而孤注一掷，并藏匿姐姐尸体的人。

故事梗概

亚瑟·柯南·道尔,英国侦探小说家。他喜爱文学,尤嗜侦探小说。柯南·道尔写了许多侦探故事,作品中的主人公夏洛克·福尔摩斯也就成了神探的典型。这些故事均收在《福尔摩斯冒险记》(1891～1892)、《福尔摩斯回忆录》(1892～1893)中。1894年,《福尔摩斯回忆录》出版后,作家对此类题材开始感到厌倦,他急于想结束侦探故事的创作,于是就在《最后一案》中让他的主人公福尔摩斯因公殉职,从悬崖上失足身亡。但是广大读者出于对福尔摩斯的喜爱,纷纷给柯南·道尔写信以示抗议。作家无奈,只好又让他笔下的福尔摩斯复活,再继续进行侦探活动,故事自然也就得以继续下去。这便是后来创作并收在《福尔摩斯的归来记》(1905)中以《空屋》(让福尔摩斯死里逃生)为开端的十一个侦探短篇。

本书中收录的十篇作品选自于《福尔摩斯回忆录》、《福尔摩斯归来记》和《福尔摩斯冒险记》,其中,《博斯科姆比溪谷秘案》、《蓝宝石案》和《工程师大拇指案》选自《福尔摩斯冒险记》,《空屋》、《跳舞的人》、《米沃尔顿》、《六座拿破仑半身像》、《第二块血迹》选自于《福尔摩斯归来记》,《吸血鬼》和《肖斯科姆别墅》选自《新探案》。小说结构严密,丝丝入扣,情节起伏跌宕,引人入胜。它不断从各个方面提出各种问题,吸引读者去寻求答案,不忍释手。此外,它还常常利用惊险的故事情节来扣人心弦,刺激读者的情感,使读者既感到恐怖,又欲罢不能,从而留下深刻的印象。小说内容本身涉及英国当时的社会现实,突出表现了人性、伦理、道德,以及殖民主义等问题。作品对图财害命、背信弃义、专横跋扈、巧取豪夺、强盗行凶等各种犯罪和不道德行为进行谴责,宣扬人道主义和善恶终有报的思想,十分迎合公众的心理。

小说将夏洛克·福尔摩斯刻画得栩栩如生、个性鲜明,塑造了一个既平凡又神奇的神探形象。他头戴礼帽,身着一袭黑色燕尾服,沉思之时总爱叼着那心爱的烟斗,那雄鹰般锐利的双眼能看透一切,那缜密的逻辑思维令人折服。他乘坐大家熟悉的马车,出没在雾气弥漫的伦敦街头,住在众所周知的贝克街寓所里,周旋于社会各个阶层以及形形色色的人物之间⋯⋯此外,小说以福尔摩斯的亲密助手华生医生第一人称的描述手法,也更加深了故事的生动性和真实性。

目　录

THE ADVENTURE OF THE SIX NAPOLEONS

It was no very unusual thing for Mr. Lestrade, of Scotland Yard, to look in upon Sherlock Holmes and myself of an evening and share *details* of a case upon which the detective was engaged. Occasionally, Mr. Holmes was able to give rather helpful suggestions, due to his vast knowledge and experience.

On this particular evening, however, Lestrade was rather quiet. Holmes looked *keenly* at him and asked: "Anything *remarkable* on hand?"

"Well, Mr. Holmes, there is something on my mind, but it is such an *absurd* business, that I *hesitated* to bother you about it. It has a bit to do with madness, and a strange madness, too. You wouldn't think there was anyone living at this time of day who had such a hatred of Napoleon the First that he would *commit burglary* in order to break images of the emperor."

Holmes sat up.

"Burglary? Let me hear the details."

Lestrade took out his official notebook and *refreshed* his memory from its pages.

"The first case reported was four days ago," said

he. "It was at the shop of Morse Hudson, who has a place for the sale of pictures and *statues* at Kennington Road. The assistant had left the front shop for an instant, when he heard a crash, and hurrying in he found *a plaster bust* of Napoleon lying shattered into *fragments*. It seemed just to be one of those senseless crimes which occur from time to time.

"The second case, however, was more serious, and also more singular. It occurred only last night. Not far from Morse Hudson's shop there lives a well known medical *practitioner*, named Dr. Barnicot. Being an *enthusiastic* admirer of Napoleon, he recently *purchased* from Morse Hudson two *duplicate* plaster casts of the famous head of Napoleon by the French artist, Devine. One of these he placed in his home at Kennington Road, and the other in his office at Lower Brixton. The doctor, this morning, found the cast missing from his home. It was discovered dashed into pieces in his garden."

Holmes *rubbed* his hands.

"This is certainly very novel," said he.

"Indeed, it is. And you can imagine the doctor's amazement when, on arriving at his office, he found his second bust had also been *smashed*. In neither case were there any signs which could give us a *clue* as to who had done the mischief. Now, Mr. Holmes, you have got the facts. "

"May I ask whether the two *busts* were exact duplicates of the one which was destroyed in Morse Hudson's shop?" asked Mr. Holmes.

"They were taken from the same *mould*. "

"Then, considering how many hundreds of statues of the great Emperor must exist in London, I doubt that this is a matter of hatred toward Napoleon. "

"Well, how do you explain it then?"

"I don't attempt to do so. I would only observe that there is a certain method in the gentleman's *eccentric proceedings*. For example, he appears to have been afraid of making noise, for he broke the bust outside of Dr. Barnicot's home, but at the office it was destroyed where it stood. The affair seems *absurdly trifling*, and yet it may mean something quite important. I shall *be* very much *obliged* to you, Lestrade, if you will let me hear of any fresh developments. "

The next day, Holmes received a telegram from Lestrade asking him to come immediately to an address in Kensington. In half an hour we reached the address *indicated*. It was located in a rather rough area of London. As we drove up, we found the railings in front of the house lined by a curious crowd.

"By George!" said Holmes, "With such a crowd as this, it's attempted murder at the least. Well, well, there's Lestrade at the front window, and we shall soon know all about it."

The official received us with a very *grave* face and showed us into the living room, where an *exceedingly* dirty and *agitated* elderly man, was pacing up and down. He was introduced to us as the owner of the house — Mr. Horace Harker, of the Central Press Syndicate.

"It's the Napoleon bust business again," said Lestrade. "You seemed interested last night, Mr. Holmes, so I thought perhaps you would be glad to be present now that the affair has taken a much graver turn."

"What has it turned to, then?"

"To murder. Mr. Harker, will you tell these gentlemen exactly what has occurred?"

The man in the dressing gown turned upon us with a most melancholy face.

"I've heard your name, Mr. Sherlock Holmes, and if you'll only explain this queer business, I shall be paid for my trouble in telling you the story."

Holmes sat down and listened.

"It all seems to center round that bust of Napoleon which I bought about four months ago. I picked it up cheap from Harding Brothers, two doors from the High Street Station. Anyway, this morning I was sitting in my den about three o'clock, for I work late, when I was *convinced* that I heard something downstairs. Then suddenly there came a most horrible *yell* — the most *dreadful* sound that ever I heard. I sat frozen with *horror* for a minute or two. Then I seized the *poker* and went downstairs. When I entered this room I found the window wide open, and I at once observed that the bust was missing."

"I then went and opened the front door. Stepping out into the dark, I nearly fell over a dead man, who was lying there. I ran back for a light and there was the poor fellow, a great gash in his throat and the whole place swimming in blood. I had just time to blow on my police whistle, and then I must have *fainted*, for I knew nothing more until I found a policeman standing over me in the hall."

"Well, who was the murdered man?" asked Holmes.

"There's nothing to show who he was," said Lestrade. "He is a tall man, sunburned, very powerful, not more than thirty. He is poorly dressed, and yet does not appear to be a laborer. A knife was lying in a pool of blood beside him, whether it belonged to the dead man or the killer, I do not know. There was nothing in his pockets save some string and a photograph. Here it is."

The picture represented an *alert*, sharp *featured* man, with thick *eyebrows* and a very long projection of the lower part of the face, like the muzzle of a monkey.

"And what became of the bust?" asked Holmes, after a careful study of this picture.

"It has been found in the front garden of an empty house in Campden House Road. It was broken into fragments. I am going round now to see it. Will you come?"

"Certainly," replied Holmes. "Are you coming with us to see the remains of your bust, Mr. Harker?"

The shaken journalist had seated himself at a

writing table.

"I must try and gather my thoughts so that I can write this story for this evening's paper," Harker answered. "Although, I'm so upset, I doubt I'll be able to even lift my pen."

The fragments of the bust had been found only a few hundred yards away. Holmes picked up several of the broken pieces and examined them carefully. I was convinced, from his *intent* face and his purposeful manner, that at last he was upon a clue.

"Well?" asked Lestrade.

Holmes *shrugged* his shoulders.

"It seems that we have some suggestive facts to act upon. First, the possession of this trifling bust was worth more, in the eyes of this strange criminal, than a human life. Then there is the singular fact that he did not break it in the house, or immediately outside the house."

"Well, this house is empty, so he felt safe to break it without disturbing others."

"Yes, but there is another empty house farther up the street which he must have passed before he came to this one. Why did he not break it there?"

"I give up," said Lestrade.

Holmes pointed to the street lamp above our heads.

"He could see what he was doing here, and he could not there. That was his reason."

"By Jove! That's true," said the detective. "Now that I come to think of it, Dr. Barnicot's bust was broken not far from his red lamp."

"We must remember that," said Holmes. "What steps do you *propose* to take now, Lestrade?"

"First, we ought to *identify* the dead man. When we have found who he is and who his *associates* are, we should have a good start in learning what he was doing in this area last night, and who it was who met him and killed him. Don't you think so?"

"No doubt, and yet it is not quite the way in which I should *approach* the case. But we shall each *investigate* in our own way, and meet up again tonight at six o'clock at my place to compare notes. Until then I should like to keep this photograph. Also, please tell Mr. Horace Harker that I'm convinced there is a mad killer at large, who believes himself to be Napoleon. It will be useful for his article."

Lestrade stared.

"You don't seriously believe that, do you?"

Holmes smiled.

"Don't I? Well, perhaps I don't. But I am sure that it will interest Mr. Horace Harker and the *subscribers* of the Central Press Syndicate. Now, Watson, I think that we shall find that we have a long and rather *complex* day's work before us. Good-bye, Lestrade, and good luck!"

Sherlock Holmes and I, *endeavoring* to *trace* the busts to their *source*, first rode an hour out to Kensington in order to see Mr. Morse Hudson, the art *dealer*. He was a small, stout man with a red face and a peppery manner.

"Yes, sir, it was I who sold Dr. Barnicot his two statues. *Disgraceful*, sir! No one but an anarchist would go about breaking statues. Who did I get the statues from? From Gelder & Co., in Church Street, Stepney. Do I know that photograph? Yes, I do. Why, it's Beppo. He was a kind of Italian *piecework* man, who made himself useful in the shop. He could carve a bit, and did odd jobs. The fellow left me last week, and I've heard nothing of him since. He was gone two days before the bust was smashed."

"Well, we have this Beppo as a common factor, both in Kennington and in Kensington, so that is worth a ten-mile drive," said Holmes as we *emerged* from the shop. "Now, Watson, let us make for Gelder & Co., of Stepney."

The sculpture works we looked for was located in a rough part of town, where the *outcasts* of Europe *tended* to gather. The manager, a big blond German, received us civilly and gave a clear answer to all Holmes's questions. A reference to his books showed that hundreds of casts had been taken from a marble copy of Devine's head of Napoleon, but that the three which had been sent to Morse Hudson a year or so before had been half of a *batch* of six, the other three being sent to Harding Brothers, of Kensington.

There was no reason why those six should be different from any of the other casts. He could suggest no possible cause why anyone should wish to destroy them. That was all he could tell us. But the production of the photograph had a remarkable effect upon the manager. His face *flushed* with anger, and he said: "Yes, indeed, I know him very well. About a year ago, he worked for us and caused trouble after he knifed another Italian in the street, and then he came to the works with the police on his heels. Beppo was his name. He was a good *workman* — one of the best."

"What did he get?" asked Holmes.

"The man lived and he got off with a year. I have no doubt he is out now, but he has not dared to show his nose here."

"When you referred in your book to the sale of those casts I observed that the date was June 3rd of last year. Could you give me the date when Beppo was *arrested*?"

"I could tell you roughly by the pay-list," the manager answered. "Yes," he continued, after some turning over of pages, "he was paid last on May 20th."

We thanked the manager and then turned our faces once again toward the west. The afternoon was far advanced before we were able to snatch a hasty luncheon at a restaurant. A news-bill we found at the restaurant ran a headline by Horace Harker that read: "Kensington *Outrage*: Murder by a Madman."

Holmes once or twice chuckled at the article.

"The press, Watson, is a most valuable institution, if you only know how to use it. And now, if you have quite finished, we will go see what the manager of Harding Brothers has to say."

The founder of that great store proved to be a *brisk*, *crisp* little person, very well dressed and quick, with a clear head and a ready tongue.

"Yes, sir, I have already read the account in the evening papers. Mr. Horace Harker is a customer of ours. We supplied him with the bust some months ago. We ordered three busts of that sort from Gelder & Co., of Stepney. They are all sold now. To whom? Allow me to look at our sales book a moment... Yes, we have the entries here: one to Mr. Harker you see, and one to Mr. Josiah Brown, of Chiswick, and one to Mr. Sandeford, of Lower Grove Road, Reading. No, I have never seen this face which you show me in the photograph. Have we any Italians on the staff? Yes, sir, we have several among our workpeople and cleaners. Sure, they might get a *peep* at that sales book if they wanted to; there is no particular reason for keeping a watch upon that book. Well, well, it's a very strange business, and I hope that you will let me know if anything comes of your *inquiries*."

Holmes had taken several notes during Mr. Harding's evidence, and I could see that he was thoroughly satisfied by the turn which affairs were taking. He made no remark, however, save that, unless we hurried, we should be late for our appointment with Lestrade. Sure enough, when we reached Baker Street the detective was already there, and we found him pacing up and down in a fever of *impatience*. His look of importance showed that his day's work had not been in vain.

"Well?" he asked. "What luck, Mr. Holmes?"

"I can now trace each of the busts from the beginning," Holmes answered.

"Well, Mr. Sherlock Holmes, I think I have done a better day's work than you. I have *identified* the dead man."

"You don't say so?"

"And found a cause for the crime."

"Splendid!"

"We have an inspector named Saffron Hill who makes a specialty of working undercover in the Italian Quarter. Well, he knew the man the moment he caught sight of the body. His name is Pietro Venucci, from Naples, and he is one of the greatest criminals in London. He is connected with the Mafia, which, as you know, is a secret Italian political society, *enforcing* its *decrees* by murder. The other fellow is probably an Italian also, and a member of the Mafia. My guess is that he has broken the rules in some fashion. Pietro is set upon his track. Probably the photograph we found in Pietro's pocket is the man himself, so that he may not knife the wrong person. He follows the fellow, he sees him enter a house, he waits outside for him, and in the fight he receives his own death-wound. How is that, Mr. Sherlock Holmes?"

Holmes clapped his hands approvingly.

"Excellent, Lestrade!" he cried. "But I didn't quite follow your explanation of the destruction of the busts."

"The busts! It is the murder that we are really investigating, and I tell you that I am gathering all the threads into my hands. All we need do now is go down with Hill to the Italian Quarter, find the man whose photograph we have got, and arrest him on the charge of murder. Will you come with us?"

"I think not. I fancy we can *attain* our end in a simpler way. I can't say for certain, because it all depends — well, it all depends upon a factor which is completely outside our control. But I have great hopes that if you will come with us tonight I shall be able to help you to lay him by the heels."

"Where?"

"In Chiswick."

It was agreed then that we would go together that night, after eleven o'clock. And Holmes, after sending a letter out in the post, spent the evening in rummaging among the files of the old daily papers with which one of our *lumber*-rooms was packed. When at last he *descended*, it was with *triumph* in his eyes, but he said nothing to me of his researches. For my own part, I had followed step by step the methods by which he had traced the various windings of this complex case, and I understood clearly that Holmes expected this grotesque criminal to make an attempt upon the two remaining busts, one of which, I remembered, was at Chiswick. I could not but admire the *cunning* with which my friend had inserted a wrong clue in the evening paper, so as to give the fellow the idea that he could continue his scheme without danger of being caught.

Lestrade pulled up to our door in a carriage at eleven, and together we drove to Chiswick, exiting near the address we obtained from the Harding Brothers. A short walk then brought us to the house we sought. The *occupants* had evidently retired to rest, for all was dark. Hiding in the shadow of the garden fence, we waited. Our wait was not long, and it ended in a very sudden and singular fashion.

In an instant, without the least sound to warn us of his coming, the garden gate swung open, and a dark figure, as swift and active as an ape, rushed up the garden path and disappeared against the black shadow of the house. We could hear the fellow making his way into the house through a window. After a short while, the man emerged again from the window. As he came out, we saw that he carried something white under his arm. Turning his back upon us he laid down his *burden*, and the next instant there was the sound of a sharp tap, followed by a clatter and rattle. The man was so intent upon what he was doing that he never heard our steps as we stole across the grass *plot*. With the *leap* of a tiger Holmes was on his back, and an instant later Lestrade and I had him bound. As we turned him over I saw a hideous, sickly face glaring up at us, and I knew that it was indeed the man of the photograph whom we had *secured*.

But it was not our prisoner to whom Holmes was giving his attention. Squatted on the doorstep, he was engaged in most carefully examining that which the man had brought from the house. It was a bust of Napoleon, like the one which we had seen that morning, and it had been broken into similar fragments. Carefully, Holmes held each separate piece to the light, and just as he had completed his examination the hall lights flew up, the door opened, and the owner of the house presented himself.

"Mr. Josiah Brown, I suppose?" said Holmes.

"Yes, sir. And you, no doubt, are Mr. Sherlock Holmes? I got the note, which you sent by the express *messenger*, and I did exactly what you told me. We locked every door on the inside and *awaited* developments. Well, I'm very glad to see that you have got the thief."

We were invited in for tea, however, Lestrade was anxious to get his man into safe quarters; so within a few minutes our cab had been *summoned* and we were all four upon our way to London.

The man was questioned *overnight*, but Holmes and I did not learn the results until the following evening, when we went to the police station. There we learned that the man was identified as Beppo, a rather well known criminal among the Italian *colony*. His reasons for destroying the busts were still unknown, and he refused to answer any questions upon the subject. He was still under questioning when we arrived.

Throughout the questioning, Holmes listened with polite attention, but when the bell rang, he started in his chair, and his eyes brightened. A minute later we heard steps upon the stairs, and an elderly red-faced man with sideburns was ushered in. In his right hand he carried an old-fashioned bag, which he placed upon the table.

"Is Mr. Sherlock Holmes here?"

My friend bowed and smiled. "Mr. Sandeford, of Reading, I suppose?" said he.

"Yes, sir. You wrote to me about a bust that is in my possession, saying you were prepared to pay ten pounds for it. Is that right?"

"Certainly."

"Well, I am an honest man, though not a very rich one. I can tell you I only gave fifteen *shillings* for the bust, and I think you ought to know that before I take ten pounds from you."

"Your honesty does you honor, Mr. Sandeford. But I have named that price, so I intend to stick to it."

Mr. Sandeford then opened his bag, and at last we saw placed upon our table a complete *specimen* of that bust which we had already seen more than once in fragments.

Holmes paid the fellow, kindly thanked him for coming at such short notice, and then showed him to the door.

Holmes then returned to the bust and taking his pistol by the barrel, struck Napoleon on the top of the head. The figure broke into fragments, and Holmes bent eagerly over the *shattered* remains. Next instant, with a loud shout of triumph, he held up one piece, in which a round, dark object was fixed like a plum in a *pudding*.

"Gentlemen," he cried, "let me introduce you to the famous black pearl of the Borgias. It is the most famous pearl now existing in the world, and it has been my good fortune to trace it from the Prince of Colonna's bedroom at the Dacre Hotel, where it was lost, to the *interior* of this, the last of the six busts of Napoleon which were *manufactured* by Gelder & Co., of Stepney.

"You will remember, both of you, that at the time of the theft suspicion fell upon the maid of the princess, who was an Italian, and it was proved that she had a brother in London, but we failed to trace any connection between them. The maid's name was Lucretia Venucci, and there is no doubt in my mind that this Pietro who was murdered two nights ago was the brother. I have been looking up the dates in the old files of the paper, and I find that the disappearance of the pearl was exactly two days before the arrest of Beppo for some crime of violence — an event which took place in the factory of Gelder & Co., at the very moment when these busts were being made. Beppo had the pearl in his possession. He may have stolen it from Pietro, I do not know. The main fact is that he had the pearl, and at that moment, when it was on his person, he was *pursued* by the police. He made for the factory in which he worked, and he knew that he had only a few minutes in which to conceal this *enormously* valuable prize, which would otherwise be found on him when he was searched. Six plaster casts of Napoleon were drying in the passage. He took the *opportunity* to carefully hide the pearl in one of them, *patching* it up nicely so no one would notice. Beppo then spent a year in prison, and in the meanwhile his six busts were *scattered* over London.

However, Beppo did not despair. Through a cousin who works with Gelder, he found out the retail firms who had bought the busts. He managed to find employment with Morse Hudson, and in that way tracked down three of them. The pearl was not there. Then, with the help of some Italian employee, he succeeded in finding out where the other three busts had gone. The first was at Harker's. There he was followed by his *confederate*, who held Beppo responsible for the loss of the pearl; and he *stabbed* him in the fight which followed.

"Of course, I could not say that he had not found the pearl in Harker's bust. I had not even concluded for certain that it was the pearl, but it was evident to me that he was looking for something, since he carried the bust past the other houses in order to break it in the garden which had a lamp *overlooking* it. There remained two busts, and it was obvious that he would go for the London one first. I warned the inmates of the house, so as to avoid a second *tragedy*, and we went down with the happiest results. By that time, of course, I knew for certain that it was the Borgia pearl that we were after. The name of the murdered man linked the one event with the other. There only remained a single bust — the Reading one — and the pearl must be there. I bought it in your presence from the owner — and there it lies."

We sat in silence for a moment.

"Well," said Lestrade, "I've seen you handle a good many cases, Mr. Holmes, but I don't know that I ever knew a more *workmanlike* one than that."

"Thank you!" said Holmes. And as he turned away, it seemed to me that he was more nearly moved by the softer human emotions than I had ever seen him. A moment later he was the cold and practical thinker once more. "Put the pearl in the safe, Watson,"said he. "And goodbye, Lestrade. If any little problem comes your way, I shall be happy, if I can, to give you a hint or two as to its *solution*."

注释

detail [ˈdiːteil, diˈteil] *n.* 细节

keenly [ˈkiːnli] *adv.* 敏锐地,急切地

remarkable [riˈmaːkəbl] *adj.* 非凡的,不平常的

absurd [əbˈsəːd] *adj.* 荒谬的,可笑的

hesitate [ˈheziteit] *v.* 犹豫,不愿

commit burglary 犯盗窃罪

refresh [riˈfreʃ] *v.* (使)精神振作,(使)更新

The Adventure of The Six Napoleons

statue ['stætju:] *n.* 雕像

plaster bust 石膏半身像

shiver ['ʃivə] *v.* 打碎,碎裂

fragment ['frægmənt] *n.* 碎片

practitioner [præk'tiʃənə] *n.* 从业者,开业者

enthusiastic [inˌθju:zi'æstik] *adj.* 热心的

purchase ['pə:tʃəs] *v.* 购买

duplicate ['dju:plikeit] *adj.* 复制的,副的 *n.* 复制品,副本

rub [rʌb] *v.* 搓,擦

smash [smæʃ] *v.* 打碎,粉碎

clue [klu:] *n.* 线索

bust [bʌst] *n.* 半身像,胸像

mould [məuld] *n.* 模型

eccentric [ik'sentrik] *adj.* 古怪的

proceeding [prə'si:diŋ] *n.* 行动,进行

absurdly [əb'sə:dli] *adv.* 荒谬地

trifling ['traifliŋ] *adj.* 不重要的

be obliged to sb. 受恩惠而感激某人

oblige [ə'blaidʒ] *v.* 施惠,帮…忙

indicate ['indikeit] *v.* 指示,简要说明

grave [greiv] *adj.* 严重的,严肃的

exceedingly [ik'si:diŋli] *adv.* 极度地,非常地

agitated ['ædʒiteitid] *adj.* 激动的,焦躁不安的

convinced [kən'vinst] *adj.* 深信的

yell [jel] *n.* 叫喊声

dreadful ['dredful] *adj.* 可怕的

horror ['hɔrə] *n.* 恐怖

poker ['pəukə] *n.* 拨火棍

faint [feint] *v.* 昏倒

alert [ə'lə:t] *adj.* 机警的,警惕的

featured [ˈfiːtʃəd] *adj.* 有…面部特征的

eyebrow [ˈaibrau] *n.* 眉毛

intent [inˈtent] *adj.* 专心的

shrug [ʃrʌg] *v.* 耸肩

propose [prəˈpəuz] *v.* 计划,建议

identify [aiˈdentifai] *v.* 鉴别,确定

associate [əˈsəuʃieit] *n.* 伙伴,朋友,同事

approach [əˈprəutʃ] *v.* 动手处理

investigate [inˈvestigeit] *v.* 调查,研究

subscriber [sʌbsˈkraibə] *n.* 订户

complex [ˈkɔmpleks] *adj.* 复杂的

endeavor [inˈdevə] *v.* 努力,尽力

trace [treis] *v.* 追踪,探索

source [sɔːs] *n.* 来源

dealer [ˈdiːlə] *n.* 经销商

disgraceful [disˈgreisful] *adj.* 可耻的

piecework [ˈpiːswək] *n.* 计件工作

emerge [iˈməːdʒ] *v.* 出现,显现

outcast [ˈautkɑːst] *n.* 流浪者

tend [tend] *v.* 趋向,往往是

batch [bætʃ] *n.* 一批

flush [flʌʃ] *v.* 使脸红

workman [ˈwəːkmən] *n.* 工人,工匠

arrest [əˈrest] *v.* 逮捕

outrage [ˈautreidʒ] *n.* 义愤

brisk [brisk] *adj.* 敏锐的,活泼的

crisp [krisp] *adj.* 爽快的,脆的

peep [piːp] *v.* 窥视

inquiry [inˈkwaiəri] *n.* 质询,调查

impatience [imˈpeiʃəns] *n.* 急躁

The Adventure of The Six Napoleons

dentify [ai'dentifai] *v.* 识别，鉴别

enforce [in'fɔːs] *v.* 强迫，执行

decree [di'kriː] *n.* 法令，教令

attain [ə'tein] *v.* 达到，获得

lumber ['lʌmbə] *n.* 杂物，废物

descend [di'send] *v.* 下来，下降

triumph ['traiəmf] *n.* 胜利，成功

cunning ['kʌniŋ] *n.* 狡猾，诡诈

occupant ['ɔkjuːpənt] *n.* 居住者

burden ['bəːdn] *n.* 负担

plot [plɔt] *n.* 小块土地

leap [liːp] *n.* 跳越，飞跃

secure [si'kjuə] *v.* 获得，取得

messenger ['mesindʒə] *n.* 信使

await [ə'weit] *v.* 等待

summon ['sʌmən] *v.* 号召，召唤

overnight ['əuvə'nait] *adv.* 整夜

colony ['kɔləni] *n.* 侨民，殖民地

shilling ['ʃiliŋ] *n.* 先令（1971 年以前英国货币单位）

specimen ['spesimin, -mən] *n.* 样品，标本

pistol ['pistl] *n.* 手枪

shatter ['ʃætə] *v.* 打碎

pudding ['pudiŋ] *n.* 布丁

interior [in'tiəriə] *n.* 内部

manufacture [,mænju'fæktʃə] *v.* 制造，加工

suspicion [səs'piʃən] *n.* 嫌疑，猜疑

pursue [pə'sjuː] *v.* 追赶，追击

enormously [i'nɔːməsli] *adv.* 非常地

opportunity [,ɔpə'tjuːniti] *n.* 机会

patch [pætʃ] *v.* 修补

25

scattered ['skætəd] *adj.* 分散的

confederate [kən'fedərit] *n.* 同盟者,同伙

stab [stæb] *v.* 刺伤,伤害

overlook [ˌəuvəluk] *v.* 耸出,俯瞰

tragedy ['trædʒidi] *n.* 悲剧

workmanlike ['wəːkmənlaik] *adj.* 精巧的

hint [hint] *n.* 暗示,线索

solution [səlju:ʃən] *n.* 解决

THE ADVENTURE OF THE SUSSEX VAMPIRE

Holmes had read carefully a letter which the last post had brought him. Then, with the dry chuckle, which was his nearest approach to a laugh, he *tossed* it over to me.

"What do you make of it, Watson?"

I read as follows:

"Dear Mr. Holmes,

I have been recommended to you by my lawyers, but indeed the matter is so extraordinarily **delicate** *that it is most difficult to discuss. It concerns a friend for whom I am acting. This gentleman married some five years ago a lady from Peru, whom he had met in connection with his business dealings with her father, a merchant. The lady was very beautiful, and a very loving wife, but she began to show some curious* **traits** *quite* **alien** *to her ordinarily sweet and gentle* **disposition**. *The gentleman had been married twice and he had one son by the first wife. This boy was now fifteen, a very charming and* **affectionate** *youth, though unhappily injured through an accident in childhood. Twice, the wife was caught* *in the act of* **assaulting** *this poor lad for no reason. Once she struck him with a stick and left a great* **bruise** *on his arm.*

This was a small matter, however, compared with her conduct to her own child, a dear boy just under one year of age. On one occasion about a month ago this child had been left by its nurse for a few minutes. A loud cry from the baby, as if he were in pain, called the nurse back. As she ran into the room she saw her employer, the lady, leaning over the baby and apparently biting his neck. The nurse was so horrified that she wished to call the husband, but the lady begged her not to do so and actually gave her five pounds as a price for her silence. No explanation was ever given, and for the moment the matter was passed over.

It left, however, a terrible impression upon the nurse's mind. Her **nerve** *gave way and she made a clean* **breast** *of it all to the man. To him it seemed as wild a tale as it may now seem to you. He told the nurse that she was dreaming. But while they were talking a sudden cry of pain was heard. Nurse and master rushed together to the nursery. Imagine his feelings, Mr. Holmes, as he saw his wife rise from*

Holmes.

"That's what puzzled the animal doctor. A sort of *paralysis*, he thought. But it's passing. He'll be all right soon."

"Did it come on suddenly?"

"In a single night."

"How long ago?"

"It may have been four months ago."

"Very remarkable. Very suggestive."

Just then, a tall, slim, brown-faced girl came into the room.

"She very ill," cried the girl, looking with *indignant* eyes at her master. "She no ask for food. She need doctor. I frightened stay alone with her without doctor."

Ferguson looked at me with a question in his eyes.

"I should be so glad if I could be of use," I said.

"Please, Delores," Ferguson said to the girl, "take Dr. Watson to her."

I followed the girl up the staircase and down an ancient *corridor*. At the end was an iron-*clamped* and massive door. The girl drew a key from her pocket, and the heavy *oaken* planks creaked upon their old *hinges.* I passed in and she swiftly followed, fastening the door behind her.

On the bed a woman was lying who was clearly in a high fever. She was only half-conscious, but as I entered she raised a pair of frightened but beautiful eyes and glared at me in *apprehension.* Seeing a stranger, she appeared to be *relieved* and sank back with a sigh upon the pillow. I stepped up to her with a few *reassuring* words, and she lay still while I took her pulse and temperature. Both were high, and yet my impression was that the condition was rather that of mental and nervous excitement than of any actual virus.

The woman turned her flushed and handsome face towards me.

"Where is my husband?"

"He is below and wishes to see you."

"I will not see him. Oh, what shall I do with this devil? It is finished. All is destroyed. Do what I will, all is destroyed."

The woman must have some strange *delusion.* I could not see honest Bob Ferguson in the character of devil.

"Madame," I said, "your husband loves you

dearly. He is deeply *grieved* at this happening. "

"He loves me. Yes. But do I not love him? Do I not love him even to sacrifice myself rather than break his dear heart? That is how I love him. And yet he could speak of me so. "

"He is full of grief, but he cannot understand. "

"No, he cannot understand. But he should trust. Go now. You can do nothing for me. Tell him only one thing. I want my child. I have a right to my child. That is the only message I can send him. "

She turned her face to the wall and would say no more.

I returned to the room downstairs, where Ferguson and Holmes still sat by the fire. Ferguson listened *moodily* to my account of the interview.

Just then, a youth entered the room. He was a remarkable lad, pale-faced and fair-haired, with excitable light blue eyes, which *blazed* into a sudden flame of emotion and joy as they rested upon his father. He rushed forward and threw his arms round his neck with the abandon of a loving girl.

"Dear little chap, these are my friends, Mr. Holmes and Dr. Watson, who have been persuaded to come down and spend an evening with us. "

"Is that Mr. Holmes, the detective?"

"Yes."

The youth looked at us with a very *penetrating* and, as it seemed to me, unfriendly gaze.

"What about your other child, Mr. Ferguson?" asked Holmes. "Might we make the *acquaintance* of the baby?"

"Ask Mrs. Mason to bring the baby down," said Ferguson. The boy went off with a curious sort of walk, which told my *surgical* eyes that he was suffering from a weak spine. *Presently* he returned, and behind him came a tall woman bearing in her arms a very beautiful child, dark-eyed, golden-haired, a wonderful mixture of the Saxon and the Latin. Ferguson was evidently devoted to it, for he took it into his arms and spoke to it most tenderly.

It was at this moment that I chanced to glance at Holmes and saw a most singular *intentness* in his expression. His eyes, which had glanced for a moment at father and child, were now fixed with eager curiosity upon the window at the other side of the room. Then he smiled, and his eyes came back to the baby. On its neck there was a small, red mark. Without speaking, Holmes examined it carefully. Turning to the nurse, he said that he wished to speak with her alone for a moment. He took her aside and spoke *earnestly* for a few minutes. The woman, who seemed to be a sour, silent kind of creature, soon *withdrew* with the child.

"What is the nurse, Mrs. Mason, like?" asked Holmes.

"Not very prepossessing *externally*, as you can see, but a heart of gold, and devoted to the child," answered Ferguson.

"Do you like her, Jack?" Holmes turned suddenly upon the boy.

The boy's expressive mobile face shadowed over, and he shook his head.

"Jacky has very strong likes and dislikes," said Ferguson, putting his arm round the boy. "Luckily, I am one of his likes. Now run away, little Jacky."

He watched his son with loving eyes until he disappeared.

Turning to me, Holmes asked: "Is the lady capable of seeing us, Watson?"

"She is ill, but she is quite *rational*."

"Very good. It is only in her presence that we can clear the matter up. Let us go up to her."

"She will not see me," cried Ferguson.

"Oh, yes, she will," said Holmes. He wrote a few lines upon a sheet of paper. "Watson, will you have the goodness to give the lady this note?"

I *ascended* again and handed the note to Dolores, who *cautiously* opened the door. A minute later I heard a cry from within, a cry in which joy and surprise seemed to be blended. Dolores looked out.

"She will see them," said she.

At my *summons* Ferguson and Holmes came up. As we entered the room Ferguson took a step or two towards his wife, who had raised herself in the bed, but she held out her hand to keep him away.

"Now, Mr. Ferguson," began Holmes, "let me first say what will ease your mind. Your wife is a very good and a very loving woman."

Ferguson sat up with a cry of joy.

"Prove that, Mr. Holmes, and I am your debtor forever."

"I will do so, but in doing so I must wound you deeply in another direction. Now, you had seen the lady rise from the child's bedside with blood upon her lips."

"I did."

"Did it not occur to you that a bleeding wound may be sucked for some other purpose than to draw the blood from it, say rather to draw poison from it?"

"Poison!"

"A South American household. My instinct felt the presence of those weapons upon the wall before my eyes ever saw them. If the child were *pricked* with one of those arrows dipped in some *devilish* drug, it would mean death if the poison were not sucked out. And the dog! If one were to use such a poison, would one not try it first in order to see that it had not lost its power? Your wife feared such an attack. She saw it made and saved the child's life, and yet she *shrank* from telling you all the truth, for she knew how you loved the boy and feared *lest* it break your heart."

"Jacky!"

"I watched him as you held the baby just now. His face was clearly reflected in the glass of the window where the *shutter* formed a background. I saw such *jealousy*, such cruel hatred, as I have seldom seen in a human face."

"My Jacky?"

"You have to face it, Mr. Ferguson. It is the

more painful because it is a *distorted* love, a crazy, *exaggerated love for you, and possibly for his dead mother, which has prompted* his action. His very soul is *consumed* with hatred for this splendid child, whose health and beauty are a contrast to his own weakness. Have I spoken the truth, madam?"

The lady was sobbing, with her face buried in the pillows. Now she turned to her husband.

"How could I tell you, Bob? I felt the blow it would be to you. It was better that I should wait and that it should come from some other lips than mine. When this gentleman, who seems to have powers of magic, wrote that he knew all, I was glad."

"I think a year at sea would be my prescription for Master Jacky," said Holmes, rising from his chair.

Ferguson was standing by the bed, choking, his hands *outstretched* and *quivering*.

"This, I fancy, is the time for our exit, Watson," said Holmes in a whisper. "If you will take one *elbow* of the too faithful Dolores, I will take the other. There, now," he added as he closed the door behind him, "I think we may leave them to settle the rest among themselves."

The Adventure of The Sussex Vampire

注释

toss [tɔs] *v.* 投,掷

delicate [ˈdelikit] *adj.* 棘手的,微妙的

trait [treit] *n.* 特性

alien [ˈeiljən] *adj.* 相异的

disposition [dispəˈziʃən] *n.* 性格倾向

affectionate [əˈfekʃənit] *adj.* 亲爱的,挚爱的

assault [əˈsɔːlt] *v.* 攻击,袭击

bruise [bruːz] *n.* 撞伤,擦伤

nerve [nəːv] *n.* 神经

breast [brest] *n.* 胸部,胸怀

confine [kənˈfain] *v.* 限制,禁闭

vampirism [ˈvæmpaiərizəm] *n.* 吸人膏血,榨取他人

agency [ˈeidʒənsi] *n.* 代理处,机构

isolated [ˌaisəleitid] *adj.* 隔离的,孤立的

dwell [dwel] *v.* 居住

deputy [ˈdepjuti] *n.* 代理人

swear [swɛə] *v.* 发誓

inoffensive [ˌinəfensiv] *adj.* 无害的,不冒犯人的

cripple [ˈkripl] *n.* 跛子

twist [twist] *v.* 扭曲

spine [spain] *n.* 脊骨

tropical [ˈtrɔpikl] *n.* 热情的;热带的

watercolor [ˈwɔːtəkʌlə] *n.* 水彩画

hind [haind] *adj.* 后边的

irregularly [iˈregjuləli] *adv.* 不规则地

lick [ˈlik] *v.* 舔

paralysis [pəˈrælisis] *n.* 麻痹,瘫痪

indignant [in'dignənt] *adj.* 愤怒的,愤慨的

corridor ['kɔridɔ:] *n.* 走廊

clamp [klæmp] *v.* 夹住,夹紧

oaken ['əukən] *adj.* 橡木制的

hinge [hindʒ] *n.* 铰链,枢纽

apprehension [ˌæpri,henʃən] *n.* 忧惧

relieved [ri'livd] *adj.* 放心的

reassuring [riə'ʃuəriŋ] *adj.* 安心的,可靠的

delusion [di'lu:ʒən] *n.* 错觉

grieved [gri:vd] *adj.* 伤心的

moodily [mu:dili] *adv.* 忧郁地

blaze [bleiz] *v.* 激发,燃烧

penetrating ['penitreitiŋ] *adj.* 敏锐的,明察秋毫的

acquaintance [ə'kweintəns] *n.* 相识,熟人

surgical ['sə:dʒikəl] *adj.* 外科医生的

presently ['prezəntli] *adv.* 不久

intentness [in'tentnis] *n.* 专注

earnestly ['ə:nistli] *adv.* 认真地,诚挚地

sour ['səuə] *adj.* 为人乖僻的,尖酸的

withdraw [wiðdrɔ:] *v.* 退出

externally [ˌeks'tə:nlli] *adv.* 外表上,外形上

rational ['ræʃənl] *adj.* 理性的

ascend [ə'send] *v.* 攀登,上升

cautiously ['kɔ:ʃəsli] *adv.* 慎重地

summons ['sʌmənz] *n.* 召唤

prick [prik] *v.* 刺,戳

devilish ['devliʃ] *adj.* 恶毒的,非常的

shrink [ʃriŋk] *v.* 退缩,回避

lest [lest] conj. 唯恐,以免

shutter ['ʃʌtə] *n.* 百叶窗

The Adventure of The Sussex Vampire

jealousy [ˈdʒeləsi] *n.* 嫉妒

distorted [disˈtɔːtid] *adj.* 扭曲的

exaggerated [igˈzædʒəreitid] *adj.* 夸张的

prompt [prɔmpt] *v.* 鼓动,促使

consume [kənˈsjuːm] *v.* 消耗,消灭

outstretched [ˈautstretʃt] *adj.* 伸出的

quivering [ˈkwivəriŋ] *adj.* 颤抖的

elbow [ˈelbəu] *n.* 肘

THE BOSCOMBE VALLEY MYSTERY

We were seated at breakfast one morning, my wife and I, when the maid brought in a telegram from Sherlock Holmes asking if I could *accompany* him to Boscombe Valley for a few days, for he had been called there in connection with a recent crime. He was to leave that day.

My wants were few and simple, so that in no time I was in a cab with my travel bag, rattling away to Paddington Station. I met Sherlock Holmes at the platform.

Upon boarding, I found we had the carriage to ourselves save for an *immense* litter of papers which Holmes had brought with him.

"Have you heard anything of the case?" he asked.

"Not a word. I have not seen a paper for some days. "

"It seems, from what I gather, to be one of those simple cases which are so extremely difficult. The more *featureless* and *commonplace* a crime is, the more difficult it is to bring it home. In this case, however, they have established a very serious case against the son of the murdered man."

"It is a murder, then?"

"Well, it is thought to be so. I shall take nothing for granted until I have the opportunity of looking personally into it. Here is the state of things as I understand it. The largest landowner in that part is a Mr. John Turner, who made his money in Australia and returned some years ago to the old country. One of the farms he held, that of Hatherley, was let to Mr. Charles McCarthy, who also had lived in Australia. The men had known each other in the *colonies*, and apparently became good enough friends to want to live near one another. Turner gave McCarthy his best farm to live on rent-free with his eighteen-year-old son. Both men are unmarried, and Turner has a daughter the same age as McCarthy's son.

On June 3rd, that is, on Monday last, McCarthy left his house at Hatherley about three in the afternoon and walked down to the Boscombe Pool. He had informed his servant that he had an appointment of importance there at three. From that appointment he never came back alive.

"From Hatherley Farmhouse to the Boscombe Pool is a quarter of a mile, and two people saw him as he passed over this ground. A few minutes later, James McCarthy, the son, was seen heading in the same direction with a hunting gun under his arm.

"A girl of fourteen, Patience Moran, who is the daughter of the *lodge*-keeper of the Boscombe Valley *estate*, was in one of the woods picking flowers, when she saw Mr. McCarthy and his son at the pool, having a violent quarrel. She heard Mr. McCarthy using very strong language to his son, and she saw the latter raise up his hand as if to strike his father. She was so frightened by their violence that she ran away and told her mother about what she had seen. She had hardly finished when young McCarthy came running up to the lodge to say that he had found his father dead in the wood, and to ask for the help of the lodge-keeper. He was much excited, and his right hand and sleeve were observed to be *stained* with fresh blood. On following him they found the dead body *stretched* out upon the grass beside the pool. The head had been beaten in by repeated blows of some heavy and *blunt* weapon. The injuries were such as might very well have been *inflicted* by the butt-end of his son's gun, which was found lying on the grass within a few paces of the body. Under these circumstances the young man was arrested, and found guilty of murder under the first two stages of his trial. Now his case is in the final stage, and awaiting judgment."

"I could hardly imagine a more *damning* case," I remarked. "If ever *circumstantial* evidence pointed to a criminal it does so here."

"I admit the case looks exceedingly grave against the young man, and it is very possible that he is indeed the culprit. However, there are several people in the neighborhood, and among them Miss Turner, the daughter of the neighboring landowner, who believe in his *innocence*, which is why you and I are on this train."

"I am afraid," said I, "that the facts are so obvious that you will find little credit to be gained out of this case."

"There is nothing more deceptive than an obvious fact," he answered, laughing. "Besides, there are one or two minor points which were brought out in the first stage of the trial, which are worth considering."

"What are they?"

"It appears that his arrest did not take place at

once, but after the return to Hatherley Farm. On the inspector informing him that he was a prisoner, he remarked that he was not surprised to hear it, and that it was no more than his deserts. However, he claimed to be innocent soon after. Now seeing as circumstances were so black against him, if he had appeared surprised at his own arrest, I should have looked upon it as highly *suspicious*, because such surprise or anger would not be natural under the circumstances, and yet might appear to be the best *policy* to a *scheming* man."

I shook my head. "Many men have been hanged on far slighter evidence."

"So they have. And many men have been wrongfully hanged."

"What is the young man's own account of the matter?"

"He claims to have just returned from a trip to Bristol, when he saw his father heading out toward the Boscombe pool. Hearing from the servant that his father had gone to a meeting, he decided to pay a visit to the *rabbit warren*, so he *grabbed* his gun and set out. When about a hundred yards from the pool he heard a cry of 'Cooee,' which was a signal between young McCarthy and his father. He then followed the call and found his father at the pool. Mr. McCarthy was surprised to see his son, and even angry that he should be there. An argument quickly ensued, and the son, seeing that his father was unreasonable, left him and began to walk back to the farm. "

"He then claims to have heard a terrible cry a short while later, which caused him to run back again. He found his father *expiring* upon the ground, with his head terribly injured. He held his father in his arms, and heard him say something about a 'rat' just before dying. He claims not to know how or by whom his father was killed, for he did not imagine the man to have enemies. "

"When asked what he and his father had argued about, young McCarthy refused to tell, saying it was *irrelevant* to the case. When asked if he had noticed anything unusual, he mentioned noticing something gray in color on the ground some distance from his injured father, but that when he got up to go and find help, it was no longer there. He was not sure what the gray object was, but guessed that it might have been a coat. "

"It seems to me," said I, "much of what he says only points toward his guilt: keeping the subject of their argument a secret; hearing his father call him before seeing him; and those too obviously *contrived* last words. The boy is *doomed*. "

Holmes laughed softly to himself and stretched out upon the cushioned seat. "I shall approach this case from the point of view that what this young man says is true, and we shall see where that *hypothesis* will lead us. "

It was nearly four o'clock when we at last found ourselves at the pretty little countrytown of Ross. A lean weasel-like man, secretive and sly-looking, was waiting for us upon the platform. This was Lestrade, of Scotland Yard. With him we drove to the Hereford Arms where a room had already been engaged for us.

"The case is as plain as can be," said Lestrade as we sat over tea in our room. "Still, of course, one can't refuse a lady. She had heard of you, and would have your opinion, though I repeatedly told her that there was nothing which you could do which I had not already done. "

He had hardly spoken before there rushed into the room one of the most lovely young women that I have ever seen in my life.

"Oh, Mr. Sherlock Holmes!" she cried, glancing from one to the other of us, and finally, with a woman's quick *intuition*, fastening upon my companion, "I am so glad that you have come. I have driven down to tell you so. I know that James didn't do it. I know it, and I want you to start upon your work knowing it, too. Never let yourself doubt upon that point. We have known each other since we were little children, and I know his faults as no one else does; but he is too tenderhearted to hurt a fly."

"I hope we may clear him, Miss Turner," said Sherlock Holmes. "You may rely upon my doing all that I can."

"And about his quarrel with his father, I am sure that the reason why he would not speak about it was because I was concerned in it."

"In what way?" asked Holmes.

"James and his father had many disagreements about me. Mr. McCarthy was very anxious that there should be a marriage between us. But of course James is young and has seen very little of life yet, and he *naturally did not wish to do anything like that yet. So there were quarrels, and this, I am sure, was one* of them. "

"And your father?" asked Holmes. "Was he in favor of such a union?"

"No, he was against it also. No one but Mr. McCarthy was in favor of it. " A quick *blush* passed over her fresh young face as Holmes shot one of his *keen*, questioning glances at her.

"May I see your father if I call tomorrow?"

"I am afraid the doctor won't allow it. "

"The doctor?"

"Yes, poor father has never been strong for years back, but this has broken him down completely. He has taken to his bed, and Dr. Willows says that his nervous system is shattered. Mr. McCarthy was the only man alive who had known dad in the old days in Victoria... at the mines. "

"Quite so; at the gold-mines, where, as I understand, Mr. Turner made his money. "

"Yes, certainly. "

"Thank you, Miss Turner. You have been of

material assistance to me. "

After the girl had gone, Lestrade invited Holmes to accompany him to the prison where young McCarthy was being held. There they could question him together. I, unfortunately, was not *authorized* to go. Instead, I spent the afternoon and early evening going over the facts of the case myself.

While it was easy to take Lestrade's point of view and assume the boy's guilt, I had so much *confidence* in Holmes that I could not help but scour the facts for *proof* of the boy's innocence. Unfortunately, I found little to nothing in his favor.

It was late before Sherlock Holmes returned. He came back alone, for Lestrade was staying in *lodgings* in town.

"I have seen young McCarthy," he said.

"And what did you learn from him?"

"Almost nothing. I did, however, discover why it is the boy wishes not to marry such an *appealing* woman. It seems the fellow is truly *insanely* in love with her; however, while she was away at boarding school for some time, the boy, like an idiot, got drunk and married a barmaid in Bristol. No one knows a word of this. And it was the impossibility of marriage with Ms. Turner that always led to the boy's fights with his father, who could not understand the boy's *hesitation*. It was with his barmaid wife that he had spent the last three days in Bristol, and his father did not know where he was. Mark that point. It is of importance. Fortunately, this barmaid, hearing of young McCarthy's arrest, has thrown him over *utterly* and has written to him to say that she has a husband already in the Bermuda Dockyard, so that there is really no tie between them."

"Alright, but if the father thought his son gone, who was he calling when he cried 'Cooee?'"

"That is a *crucial* point upon which the entire case depends, Watson. And I'm afraid we need more information. Tomorrow morning, we shall visit the scene of the crime."

At nine o'clock the next day, Lestrade called for us with the carriage and we set off for Hatherley Farm and the Boscombe Pool.

"There is serious news this morning," Lestrade observed. "It is said that Mr. Turner is so ill that his life is *despaired* of."

"An elderly man, I *presume?*" said Holmes.

"About sixty; but his *constitution* has been shattered by his life abroad, and he has been in failing health for some time. This business has had a very bad effect upon him."

"Indeed! That is interesting," said Holmes. "By the way, I can't seem to get my head around one odd fact. If these men were such good friends, why then was Turner so opposed to the marriage of their children? And *moreover*, why was McCarthy so *adamant* about his son *proposing*, as if there were no *obstacles* to the marriage but the son's own reservations?"

At this time, we pulled up to the front of Hatherley Farm. The first thing Sherlock Holmes was shown, were the boots Mr. McCarthy had worn. Then we made our way to Boscombe Pool.

The pool, which is a little sheet of water some fifty yards across, is *situated* at the *boundaries* between the Hatherley Farm and the private park of the wealthy Mr. Turner. Above the woods, which lined it upon the farther side, we could see the red *rooftops*, which marked the site of the rich landowner's *dwelling*.

Lestrade showed us the exact spot at which the body had been found, and, indeed, so *moist* was the ground, that I could plainly see the traces which had been left by the fall of the stricken man. Holmes seemed to see much more than that. He drew out a *lens* and lay down upon his *waterproof* to have a better view, talking all the time to himself rather than to us.

"These are young McCarthy's feet. Twice he was walking, and once he ran swiftly, so that the soles are deeply marked and the heels hardly visible. That bears out his story. He ran when he saw his father on the ground. Then here are the father's feet as he paced up and down. What is this, then? It is the butt-end of the gun as the son stood listening. And this? Ha, ha! What have we here? Tiptoes! Square, too, quite unusual boots! They come, they go, they come again of course that was for the gray *cloak*. Now where did they come from?" He ran up and down, sometimes losing, sometimes finding the track until we were well within the edge of the wood and under the shadow of the largest tree in the neighborhood. A stone was lying among the *moss*, and this he carefully examined and *retained*. Then he followed a pathway through the wood until he came to the high-road, where all traces were lost. "

After this, we all returned to our carriage and headed back to Ross, Holmes still carrying with him the stone which he had picked up in the wood.

"This may interest you, Lestrade," he re-marked, holding it out. "The murder was done with it. "

"I see no marks. "

"There are none. "

"How do you know, then?"

"The grass was growing under it. It had only lain there a few days. There was no sign of a place from where it had been taken. It corresponds with the injuries. There is no sign of any other weapon. "

"And the murderer?"

"Is a tall man, left-handed, *limps* with the right leg, wears thick shooting boots and a gray cloak, and smokes Indian cigars. Now, find the man who mat-ches this description and this case will be *solved*. "

Lestrade shrugged his shoulders. "I am a practi-cal man," he said, "and I really cannot *undertake* to go about the country looking for a left-handed gentle-man with a lame leg. I should become the *laughing-stock* of Scotland Yard. "

"All right," said Holmes quietly. " I have given you the chance. Here are your lodgings. Good-bye. "

Having left Lestrade at his rooms, we drove to our hotel, where we found lunch upon the table. While dining, Holmes talked with me more about his discoveries.

"I have hit upon two striking things, Watson. Hear me out. The first is the call of 'Cooee' by Mr. McCarthy. Seeing as he thought his son was away, let's assume this cry was meant to attract the attention of *whomever* it was that he had the appointment with. But this cry is a *distinctly* Australian cry. There is a strong *presumption* that the person whom McCarthy expected to meet him at Boscombe Pool was someone who had been in Australia. "

"I'm with you there," I said.

"Good. Now there is the problem of the father having spoken the word 'rat' just before dying. " Holmes then took a folded paper from his pocket and flattened it out on the table. "This is a map of the

Colony of Victoria. I wired to Bristol for it last night. " He put his hand over part of the map.

"What do you read?"

"ARAT," I read.

"And now?" He raised his hand.

"BALLARAT. "

"Quite so. That was the word the man *uttered*, and of which his son only caught the last two syllables. He was trying to utter the name of his murderer. So and so, of Ballarat. "

"Wonderful!" I *exclaimed*.

"We also know that the murderer could only be a man from this *district*, for the way to the pool is far too *complicated* for a stranger. "

"Quite so, but how did you learn that the man was lame?"

"The impression of his right foot was always less distinct than his left. He put less weight upon it. Why? Because he *limped*. "

"But his left-handedness. "

"The blow was struck from immediately behind, and yet was upon the left side. Now, how can that be unless it were by a left-handed man? He had stood behind that large tree during the interview between the father and son. He had even smoked there. I found the ash of a cigar, which my special knowledge of tobacco ashes enables me to pronounce as an Indian cigar."

"Holmes," I said, "I see the direction in which all this points. The culprit is..."

"Mr. John Turner," cried the hotel waiter, opening the door of our dining room, and ushering in a visitor.

The man who entered was a strange and *impressive* figure. His slow, limping step and bowed shoulders showed signs of illness, but his *enormous limbs* showed that he was possessed of unusual strength of body and of character.

"Please, sit down on the sofa," said Holmes gently. "You had my note?"

"Yes, you said that you wished to see me here to avoid *scandal*."

"Yes," said Holmes. "It is so. I know all about McCarthy."

The old man sank his face in his hands. "God help me!" he cried. "I would have spoken up sooner had it not been for my dear girl. It would break her heart — it will break her heart when she hears that I am in prison."

"It may not come to that," said Holmes. "I'm mostly concerned with getting Young McCarthy off."

"I am a dying man," said old Turner. "My doctor says it is a question whether I shall live a month. Yet I would rather die under my own roof than in a jail."

Holmes rose and sat down at the table with his pen in his hand and a *bundle* of paper before him. "Just tell us the truth," he said. "I shall write down the facts. You will sign it, and Watson here can *witness* it. Then I could produce your *confession* at the last *extremity* to save young McCarthy. I promise you that I shall not use it unless it is absolutely needed."

"Very well," said Turner, sighing deeply. "Now then, you didn't know this dead man, McCarthy. He was a devil. His *grip* has been upon me these twenty years, and he has *blasted* my life. I'll tell you first how I came to be in his power.

"In the early 60's I was a young chap and got among bad companions. Together, we took to the bush and became highway robbers. I was known as Black Jack of Ballarat. One day we attacked a party of *wagons* heading to Melbourne, carrying gold. I put my pistol to the head of the wagondriver, who was this very man McCarthy. I wish to the Lord that I had shot him then, but I spared him and left him where he was. We got away with the gold, became wealthy men, and made our way over to England without being suspected. There I determined to settle down to a quiet and respectable life. I bought this estate, which chanced to be in the market, and I set myself to do a little with my money, to make up for the way in which I had earned it. I married, too, and though my wife died young she left me my dear little Alice. All was going well when I met McCarthy by chance in Regent Street with hardly a coat to his back or a boot to his foot."

"'Here we are, Jack,' says he, touching me on the arm; 'we'll be as good as a family to you. There are two of us, me and my son, and you can have the keeping of us. If you don't — it's a fine, law-*abiding* country is England, and there's always a policeman within hail.'"

Well, down they came to the west country, there was no shaking them off, and there they have lived rent free on my best land ever since. Whatever he wanted I gave him without question, land, money, houses, until at last he asked a thing which I could not give. He asked for Alice.

"It's not that I had any dislike for his son, but his blood was McCarthy blood, and that was enough. I stood firm. McCarthy *threatened*. I braved him to do his worst. We were to meet at the pool midway between our houses to talk it over. When I went down there I found him talking with his son. "

He was urging his son to marry my daughter with as little regard for what she might think as if she were a girl from off the streets. It drove me mad to think that I and all that I held most dear should be in the power of such a man as this. I figured I'd save my girl if I could but silence that *foul* tongue. And I did it, Mr. Holmes. I would do it again, if I had to.

"His cry brought back his son; but I had gained the cover of the wood, though I was forced to go back to fetch the cloak which I had dropped in my flight. That is the true story, gentlemen, of all that occurred."

"Well, it is not for me to judge you," said Holmes as the old man signed the statement which had been drawn out. "I pray that we may never be exposed to such a temptation."

"I pray not, sir. And what do you intend to do?"

"In view of your health, nothing. You are yourself aware that you will soon have to answer for your deed at a higher court than the one here. I will keep your confession, and if McCarthy is *condemned* I shall be forced to use it. If not, it shall never be seen by *mortal* eye; and your secret, whether you be alive or dead, shall be safe with us."

"Farewell, then," said the old man *solemnly.* "Your own deathbeds, when they come, will be the easier for the thought of the peace which you have given to mine."

The man's giant *frame* then *stumbled* slowly from the room.

James McCarthy was *acquitted* on the strength of a number of objections, which had been drawn out by Holmes and *submitted* to the defending *counsel.* Old Turner lived for seven months after our interview, but he is now dead; and there is every *prospect* that the son and daughter may come to live happily together in ignorance of the black cloud which rests upon their past.

注释
___

accompany [ə'kʌmpəni] *v.* 陪伴

immense [i'mens] *adj.* 广大的,无边的

featureless [ˌfiːtʃəlis] *adj.* 无特色的,平凡的

commonplace ['kɔmənpleis] *adj.* 平凡的

colony ['kɔləni] *n.* 侨民,侨民区,殖民地

lodge [lɔdʒ] *n.* 门房,旅馆

estate [i'steit] *n.* 庄园,不动产

stained [steind] *adj.* 玷污的

stretch [stretʃ] *v.* 伸展,伸长

blunt [blʌnt] *adj.* 钝的,生硬的

inflict [in'flikt] *v.* 造成

damning ['dæmiŋ] *adj.* 毁灭的,咒骂的

circumstantial [ˌsəːkəm'stænʃəl] *adj.* 依照情况的

innocence ['inəsns] *n.* 清白,无辜

suspicious [səs'piʃəs] *adj.* 可疑的

policy ['pɔlisi] *n.* 精明的行为,权谋

scheming ['skiːmiŋ] *adj.* 诡计多端的

rabbit warren 养兔场

grab [græb] *v.* 抓取,夺取

ensue [in'sjuː] *v.* 继起

expire [iks'paiə] *v.* 断气,终止

irrelevant [iˈrelivənt] *adj.* 不相关的

contrived [kənˈtraivd] *adj.* 人为的，做作的

doomed [duːmd] *adj.* 命定的

hypothesis [haiˈpɒθisis] *n.* 假设

weasel [ˈwiːzl] *n.* 黄鼠狼，狡猾的人

intuition [ˌintju(ː)ˈiʃən] *n.* 直觉

naturally [ˈnætʃərəli] *adv.* 自然地，正常地

blush [blʌʃ] *n.* 脸红

keen [kiːn] *adj.* 敏锐的

authorized [ˈɔːθəraizd] *adj.* 经授权的

assume [əˈsjuːm] *v.* 假定，设想

confidence [ˈkɒnfidəns] *n.* 信心

proof [pruːf] *n.* 证据

lodging [ˈlɒdʒiŋ] *n.* 出租的房间

appealing [əˈpiːliŋ] *adj.* 吸引人的

insanely [inˈseinli] *adv.* 疯狂地

hesitation [ˌheziˈteiʃən] *n.* 犹豫，踌躇

utterly [ˈʌtəli] *adv.* 完全地

crucial [ˈkruːʃial,ˈkruːʃəl] *adj.* 至关紧要的

despair [disˈpɛə] *v.* 绝望，失望

presume [priˌzjuːm] *v.* 假定，假设

constitution [ˌkɒnstiˈtjuːʃən] *n.* 体质，体格

adamant [ˈædəmənt] *adj.* 固执的，强硬的

moreover [mɔːˈrəuvə] *adv.* 而且，此外

propose [prəˈpouz] *v.* 求婚

obstacle [ˈɒbstəkl] *n.* 障碍

situate [ˈsitjueit] *v.* 使位于

boundary [ˈbaundəri] *n.* 边界

rooftop [ˈruːftɒp] *n.* 屋顶

The Boscombe Valley Mystery

dwelling ['dweliŋ] *n.* 住处

moist [mɔist] *adj.* 潮湿的

lens [lenz] *n.* 透镜

waterproof ['wɔːtəpruːf] *adj.* 防水的

sole [soul] *n.* 鞋底,脚底

cloak [kləuk] *n.* 斗篷

moss [mɔs] *n.* 苔,藓

retain [ri'tein] *v.* 保留

limp [limp] *v.* 跛行

solve [sɔlv] *v.* 解决

undertake ['ʌndə'teik] *v.* 承担,担任

laughingstock ['lɑːfiŋstɔk] *n.* 笑柄

whomever [huːm'evə] *pron.* whoever 的宾格形式

pro [prəu] *n.* 任何人,无论谁

distinctly [dis'tiŋktli] *adv.* 显然,清楚地

presumption [pri'zʌmpʃən] *n.* 假定

utter ['ʌtə] *v.* 发出,做声

exclaim [ik'skleim] *v.* 呼喊,大叫

district ['distrikt] *n.* 区域

complicated ['kɔmplikeitid] *adj.* 复杂的,难解的

distinct [dis'tiŋkt] *adj.* 清楚的

limp [limp] *v.* 跛行

impressive [im'presiv] *adj.* 给人印象深刻的

enormous [i'nɔːməs] *adj.* 巨大的

limb [lim] *n.* 肢,分支

scandal ['skændl] *n.* 流言蜚语,丑闻

bundle ['bʌndl] *n.* 捆,扎

confession [kən'feʃən] *v.* 承认

extremity [iks'tremiti] *n.* 极端,非常手段

witness ['witnis] *v.* 目击

grip [grip] *n.* 掌握,控制

blast [,blɑːst] *v.* 毁灭,损害

wagon ['wægən] *n.* 货车,四轮马车

abide [ə'baid] *v.* 遵守

hail [heil] *n.* 招呼

threaten ['θretn] *v.* 威胁

foul [faul] *adj.* 邪恶的,恶劣的

condemn [kən'dem] *v.* 判刑

mortal ['mɔːtl] *adj.* 人类的

solemnly ['sɔləmli] *adv.* 严肃地

frame [freim] *n.* 结构,体格

stumble ['stʌmbl] *v.* 蹒跚

acquit [ə'kwit] *v.* 宣告无罪

submit [səb'mit] *v.* 递交

counsel ['kaunsəl] *n.* 辩护律师

prospect ['prɔspekt] *n.* 前景,期望

THE ADVENTURE OF THE DANCING MEN

Holmes had been seated for some hours in silence over his chemistry lab, where he was *brewing* an especially *odorous* product, when suddenly he said to me: "So, Watson, you do not propose to invest in South African *securities*?"

I gave a start of astonishment.

"How on earth do you know that?" I asked.

"It's quite simple: One. You had chalk between your left finger and thumb when you returned from the club last night. Two. You put chalk there when you play billiards, to steady the *cue*. Three. You never play billiards except with Thurston. Four. You told me, four weeks ago, that Thurston had an option on some South African property which would *expire* in a month, and which he desired you to share with him. Five. Your checkbook is locked in my drawer, and you have not asked for the key. Six. You do not propose to invest your money in this manner."

"How absurdly simple!" I cried.

"Quite so!" said he, a little annoyed. "Every problem becomes very childish when once it is explained to you. Here is an unexplained one. See what you can make of that, friend Watson."

He tossed a sheet of paper upon the table, and turned once more to his chemical *analysis*. I looked with amazement at the absurd picture upon the paper.

"Why, Holmes, it is a child's drawing," I cried.

"So it seems, anyway. Ah! There's the door-bell. It must be Mr. Hilton Cubitt, the man who sent me this paper."

A heavy step was heard upon the stairs, and an instant later there entered a tall, healthy-looking, clean-shaven gentleman. Having shaken hands with each of us, he asked what we thought about the picture he had sent.

"At first sight it would appear to be some childish joke," Holmes commented. "It consists of a number of absurd little figures dancing across the paper upon which they are drawn. Why should you attribute any importance to so grotesque an object?"

"I never should, Mr. Holmes. But my wife does. It is frightening her to death."

"You gave me a few particulars in your letter, but I should be very much obliged if you would kindly go over it all again for the benefit of my friend, Dr.

Watson. "

"Alright. Last year I came up to London for the Jubilee, and I happened to meet an young American lady — Elsie Patrick. In some way we became friends, until before my month was up I was as much in love as a man could be. We were quietly married at the courthouse, and we returned to Norfolk, my home, a wedded couple.

"Elsie was very straight about our courtship. She told me she had had some very disagreeable *associations* in her life that she wished to forget all about. She made me promise never to ask about her past, and I have kept my word ever since. And this year of marriage has been a truly happy one. But about a month ago my wife received a letter from America. I saw the American stamp. She turned deadly white, read the letter, and threw it into the fire. She said nothing about it afterwards, and I asked no questions, for a promise is a promise, but she has never known an easy hour from that moment. There is always a look of fear upon her face — a look as if she were waiting and expecting. "

"Then, about a week ago, I found on one of the windows a number of absurd little dancing figures like these upon the paper. They were drawn with chalk. My wife took it very seriously, and begged me if any more came to let her see them. Just yesterday morning I found this paper lying in the garden. I showed it to Elsie, and down she dropped in a dead *faint*. It was then that I wrote and sent the paper to you, Mr. Holmes."

"Don't you think, Mr. Cubitt," said he, at last, "that your best plan would be to make a direct *appeal* to your wife, and to ask her to share her secret with you?"

"A promise is a promise, Mr. Holmes. If Elsie wished to tell me she would. If not, it is not for me to force her confidence. But I am *justified* in taking my own line — and I will."

"Then I will help you with all my heart. In the first place, have you heard of any strangers being seen in your neighborhood?"

"No. But we have several small watering places not very far away. And the farmers take in *lodgers*."

"These pictures have evidently a meaning. But this particular *sample* is so short that I can do nothing, and the facts which you have brought me are so *indefinite* that we have no basis for an *investigation*.

I would suggest that you return to Norfolk, and that you take an exact copy of any fresh dancing men which may appear. When you have collected some fresh evidence, come to me again. "

Hilton Cubitt did as Holmes suggested, and did not return to us until two weeks later. When he came into our office he looked worried and depressed.

"It's getting on my nerves, this business, Mr. Holmes," said he, as he sank, like a *wearied* man, into an armchair. "It is just killing my wife by inches. She's wearing away under it — just wearing away before my eyes. "

"Has she said anything yet?"

"No, Mr. Holmes, she has not. And yet there have been times when the poor girl has wanted to speak, and yet could not quite bring herself to *take the plunge*. "

"But you have found out something for yourself?"

"A good deal, Mr. Holmes. I have several fresh dancingmen pictures for you to examine, and, what is more important, I have seen the fellow. "

"What, the man who draws them?"

"Yes, I saw him at his work. But I will tell you

everything in order. When I got back after my visit to you, the very first thing I saw next morning was a fresh crop of dancing men. I took an exact copy, and here it is. " He unfolded a paper and laid it upon the table.

"Excellent!" said Holmes. "Please, continue. "

"Two mornings later a fresh *inscription* appeared. I have a copy of it here. "

Holmes rubbed his hands and chuckled with delight.

"Three days later a message was left written upon paper, and placed under a rock in the garden. Here it is. The characters are, as you see, exactly the same as the last one. After that I determined to lie in wait, so I got out my *revolver* and I sat up in my study. My wife begged me to go to bed, but I refused. And then suddenly, a dark, *creeping* figure appeared outside our window. He seemed to busy with something at the black shed next to our garden. Seizing my pistol, I was rushing out, when my wife threw her arms round me and held me with all her strength. At last I got clear, but by the time I had opened the door and reached the shed the creature was gone. He had left a trace of his presence, however, for there on the door of the shed was drawn the very same arrangement of dancing men which had already twice appeared, and which I have copied on that paper. I was angry with my wife that night for having held me back when I might have caught the man. She said that she feared that I might come to harm. And though I doubted at first, now I am sure that it was indeed my own safety that was in her mind. There's the whole case, and now I want your advice as to what I ought to do."

"Leave me these papers, and I think that it is very likely that I shall be able to pay you a visit shortly," said Holmes.

The moment that Hilton Cubitt's broad back had disappeared through the door my comrade rushed to the table, laid out all the slips of paper containing dancing men in front of him, and threw himself into an *intricate* and *elaborate calculation*. For two hours I watched him as he covered sheet after sheet of paper with figures and letters, so completely absorbed in his task that he had evidently forgotten my presence. Finally he sprang from his chair with a cry of satisfaction, and walked up and down the room rubbing his hands together. Then he wrote a long telegram upon a cable form.

"If my answer to this is as I hope, you will have a very pretty case to add to your collection, Watson," said he. " I expect that we shall be able to go down to Norfolk tomorrow, and to take our friend some very definite news as to the secret of his annoyance."

But there was a delay in that answering telegram, and two days of impatience followed, during which Holmes pricked up his ears at every ring of the bell. Finally, there came a letter from Hilton Cubitt. He *enclosed* a copy of a long inscription which had recently been found. Holmes bent over the picture for some minutes, and then suddenly sprang to his feet with a look of surprise and *dismay*.

"We have let this affair go far enough," said he. "Is there a train to North Walsham tonight?"

I turned up the train schedule. The last had just gone.

"Then we shall breakfast early and take the very first in the morning," said Holmes. "Our presence is most urgently needed. Ah! Here is our expected telegram. Quite as I expected, this message makes it even more essential that we should not lose an hour in letting Hilton Cubitt know how matters stand."

So, indeed, it proved, and as I come to the dark conclusion of a story which had seemed to me to be only childish and *bizarre*, I experience once again the dismay and horror with which I was filled.

The next day, we had hardly arrived at North Walsham, and mentioned the name of our destination, when the station manager hurried towards us.

"I suppose that you are the detectives from London?" said he.

A look of annoyance passed over Holmes's face.

"What makes you think such a thing?"

"Because Inspector Martin from Norwich has just passed through. But maybe you are the surgeons. She's not dead — or wasn't by last accounts. You may be in time to save her yet — though it would be for her to be hanged."

"We are going to Riding Thorpe Manor," said Holmes, "but we have heard nothing of what has passed there."

"It's a terrible business," said the manager. "They are shot, both Mr. Hilton Cubitt and his wife. She shot him and then herself — so the servants say. He's dead and her life is despaired of."

Without a word Holmes hurried to a carriage,

and during the long seven miles' drive he never opened his mouth. Seldom have I seen him so utterly unhappy.

As we drove up to the front door of Riding Thorpe, I observed in front of it, beside the tennis *lawn*, the black shed and the garden with which we had such strange associations. A well dressed little man, with a quick, alert manner and a *waxed* moustache introduced himself as Inspector Martin, of the Norfolk police.

"Let me just say, Mr. Holmes," said he, "I plan to fully *cooperate* with you in this investigation. I have heard much about you and have the *utmost* respect for your work."

"Thank you, Inspector," answered Holmes. "Let's begin our investigation, then, immediately."

The local surgeon, an old, white-haired man, had just come down from Mrs. Hilton Cubitt's room, and he reported that her injuries were serious, but not necessarily fatal. On the question of whether she had been shot or had shot herself, he would not *venture* to express any decided opinion. There was only the one pistol found in the room, two barrels of which had been emptied. Mr. Hilton Cubitt had been shot through the heart. It was equally *conceivable* that he had shot her and then himself, or that she had been the criminal, for the revolver lay upon the floor midway between them.

"Who found them?" asked Holmes.

"The servants. "

"Then I think we had better hear their story at once. "

Holmes questioned the servants in the old hall. While he did so, I could read in his eyes a set purpose to devote his life to this quest until the client whom he had failed to save should at last be avenged.

The two women told their story clearly enough. They had been *aroused* from their sleep by the sound of gunshot, which had been followed a minute later by a second one. Together they had descended the stairs, and found their master lying upon his face in the center of the room. He was quite dead. Near the window his wife was crouching, her head leaning against the wall. She was horribly wounded, and the side of her face was red with blood. The passage, as well as the room, was full of smoke and the smell of powder. The window was certainly shut and fastened upon the inside. Both women were positive upon the point. So far as they knew, there had never been any quarrel between husband and wife. They had always looked upon them as a very united couple.

Holmes then thoroughly examined the room. Mr. Cubitt's *disordered* dress showed that he had been *hastily* aroused from sleep. The *bullet* had been fired at him from the front, and had remained in his body, after penetrating the heart. His death had certainly been *instantaneous* and painless.

"I suppose, Doctor, you have not recovered the bullet which wounded the lady?" asked Holmes.

"A serious operation will be necessary before that can be done. But there are still four cartridges in the revolver. Two have been fired and two wounds inflicted, so that each bullet can be accounted for."

"So it would seem," said Holmes. "Perhaps you can account also for the bullet which has so obviously struck the edge of the window?"

He had turned suddenly, and his long, thin finger was pointing to a hole, which had been drilled right through the lower window ledge, about an inch above the bottom.

"By George!" cried the inspector. "You are certainly right, sir. Then a third shot has been fired, and therefore a third person must have been present. But who could that have been, and how could he have got away?"

"That is the problem which we are now about to solve," said Sherlock Holmes. "You remember, Inspector Martin, the servants said that on leaving their room they were at once conscious of a smell of powder?"

"Yes, sir. "

"It suggested that at the time of the firing, the window as well as the door of the room had been open. Otherwise the *fumes* of powder could not have been blown so rapidly through the house. Thus, feeling sure that the window had been open at the time of the tragedy, I conceived that there might have been a third person in the affair, who stood outside this opening and fired through it. Any shot directed at this person might hit the window ledge. I looked, and there, sure enough, was the bullet mark!"

"But how came the window to be shut and fastened?"

"The woman's first instinct would be to shut and fasten the window. But wait! What is this?"

It was a lady's purse which stood upon the study

table — a trim little handbag of crocodile-skin and silver. Holmes opened it and turned the contents out. Inside, there were twenty fifty-pound notes of the Bank of England.

"This must be preserved, for it will figure in the trial," said Holmes, as he handed the bag with its contents to the inspector. "Now, as to the third bullet... the servants only mentioned hearing two shots fired. It must have been the case that two shots occurred at the same time, sounding as one. Now let's have a look at the garden."

Upon arriving in the garden, we found the flowers were trampled down, and the soft soil was stamped all over with footmarks. Large, *masculine* feet they were, with *peculiarly* long, sharp toes.

Holmes hunted about among the grass and leaves and found a bullet cartridge.

"I really think, Inspector Martin, that our case is almost complete. I have the threads of this affair all in my hand. Even if this lady should never recover consciousness, we can still reconstruct the events of last night and insure that justice be done. First of all, I wish to know whether there is any inn in this neighborhood known as 'Elrige's.'"

After asking the servants, only the *stable* boy could throw a light upon the matter by remembering that a farmer of that name lived some miles off, in the direction of East Ruston.

Holmes thought for a little, and then a curious smile played over his face.

"Saddle a horse, my lad," said he. "I shall wish you to take a note to Elrige's Farm."

He took from his pocket the various slips of the dancing men. With these in front of him, he worked for some time at the study table. Finally, he handed a note to the boy, with directions to put it into the hands of the person to whom it was addressed, and especially to answer no questions of any sort which might be put to him. I saw the outside of the note, addressed to Mr. Abe Slaney, Elrige Farm.

When the youth had been *dispatched* with the note, Sherlock Holmes remarked that the business was now out of our hands, and that we must while away the time as best we might until we could see what was in store for us. The doctor had *departed* to his patients, and only the inspector and myself remained.

"I think that I can help you to pass an hour in an

interesting and *profitable* manner," said Holmes, drawing his chair up to the table, and spreading out in front of him the various papers upon which were the dancing men. "I am fairly familiar with all forms of secret writings, and am myself the author of a trifling article upon the subject, in which I analyze one hundred and sixty separate codes, but I confess that this is entirely new to me. Having once recognized, however, that the symbols stood for letters, and having applied the rules which guide us in all forms of secret writings, the solution was easy enough. In the first message four out of fifteen symbols were the same, so it was reasonable to set this down as representing the letter E, for this letter is the most commonly found in the English language. It is true that in some cases the figure was bearing a flag, and I quickly *perceived* this to mark a break in the sentence. In my second interview with Mr. Hilton Cubitt he was able to give me two other short sentences and one message, which appeared — since there was no flag — to be a single word. Here are the symbols. Now, in the single word I have already got the two E's coming second and fourth in a word of five letters. It might be 'lever,' or 'never.' There can be no question that the latter as a reply to an appeal is far the most probable, and the circumstances pointed to its being a reply written by the lady. We can now identify the letters N, V, and R.

"It occurred to me that a combination which contained two E's with three letters between might very well stand for the name 'Elsie.' On examination I found that such a combination formed the *termination* of the message which was three times repeated. It was certainly some appeal to 'Elsie.' In this way I had got my L, S, and I. But what appeal could it be? There were only four letters in the word which preceded 'Elsie,' and it ended in E. Surely the word must be 'COME.' I tried all other four letters ending in E, but could find none to fit the case. So now I was in possession of C, O, and M, and I was in a position to attack the first message once more, dividing it into words and putting dots for each symbol which was still unknown. So treated, it worked out in this fashion:

. M. ERE. . E SL. NE.

"Now the first letter can only be A, which is a most useful discovery, since it occurs no fewer than three times in this short sentence, and the H is also apparent in the second word. Now it becomes:

AM HERE A. E SLANE.

"Or, filling in the obvious *vacancies* in the name:

AM HERE ABE SLANEY

"I had so many letters now that I could proceed with considerable confidence to the second message, which worked out in this fashion:

A . ELRI. ES .

"Here I could only make sense by putting T and G for the missing letters, and supposing that the name was that of some house or inn at which the writer was staying. "

"I had every reason to suppose that this Abe Slaney was an American, since Abe is an American *contraction*, and since a letter from America had been the starting-point of all the trouble. I therefore *cabled* to my friend, Wilson Hargreave, of the New York Police Bureau, and asked him whether he knew the name of Abe Slaney. Here is his reply: ' The most dangerous criminal in Chicago. ' On the very evening upon which I had his answer, Hilton Cubitt sent me the last message from Slaney. Working with known letters, it took this form:

ELSIE. RE. ARE TO MEET. O. R GO.

"The addition of two P's, a Y, U, and D completed a message which showed me that the man was proceeding from *persuasion* to *threats*. I at once came to Norfolk with my friend and colleague, Dr. Watson, but, unhappily, only in time to find that the worst had already occurred."

"Now, if I'm not mistaken, I believe this man walking up the drive is Abe Slaney himself."

A tall, handsome man was indeed *striding* up the path toward the front door. He acted as if the place belonged to him, and we heard his loud, confident knock at the door.

"I think, gentlemen," said Holmes, quietly, "that we had best take up our position behind the door. Every *precaution* is necessary when dealing with such a fellow."

We waited in silence for a minute. Then the door opened and the man stepped in. In an instant Holmes clapped a pistol to his head, and Martin slipped chains over his *wrists*. It was all done so swiftly that the fellow was helpless before he knew that he was attacked. He glared from one to the other of us with a pair of *blazing* black eyes. Then he burst into a bitter laugh.

"Well, gentlemen, you have the drop on me this time. I seem to have knocked up against something hard. But I came here in answer to a letter from Mrs. Hilton Cubitt. Don't tell me that she is in this?"

"Mrs. Hilton Cubitt was seriously injured, and is at death's door," replied Holmes.

The man gave a hoarse cry of grief, which rang through the house.

"You're crazy!" he cried, fiercely. "It was he that was hurt, not she. Who would have hurt little Elsie?"

"She was found badly wounded, by the side of her dead husband."

He sank with a deep groan on the sofa and buried his face in his chained hands. For five minutes he was silent. Then he raised his face once more, and spoke with the cold *composure* of despair.

"If I shot the man he had his shot at me, and there's no murder in that. But if you think I could have hurt that woman, then you don't know either me or her. I tell you, there was never a man in this world loved a woman more than I loved her. I had a right to her. She was *pledged* to me years ago, for her father was the leader of our *gang* in Chicago.

Who was this Englishman that he should come between us? I tell you that I had the first right to her, and that I was only claiming my own. "

"You have ended by bringing about the death of a noble man and driving his wife to *suicide*. That is your record in this business, Mr. Abe Slaney, and you will answer for it to the law. "

He opened one of his hands, and looked at a note crumpled up in his palm. "If the lady is hurt as bad as you say, who was it that wrote this note?" He tossed it forward on to the table.

"I wrote it, to bring you here. "

"You wrote it? There was no one on earth outside *the Joint* who knows the secret of the dancing men. How came you to write it?"

"What one man can invent another can discover," said Holmes. "There is a cab coming to convey you to Norwich, Mr. Slaney. But meanwhile, you can tell us exactly what occurred here. "

"Elsie and I were engaged, but then she found out the sort of business I was involved in and she left me, running off to England. It was only after her marriage to this Englishman that I was able to find out where she was. I wrote to her, but got no answer. After that I came over, and as letters were no use, I put my messages where she could read them.

"She sent me a letter, begging me to go away. She said that she would come down when her husband was asleep at three in the morning, and speak with me through the end window, if I would go away afterwards and leave her in peace. She came down and brought money with her, trying to *bribe* me to go. This made me mad, and I caught her arm and tried to pull her through the window. At that moment, in rushed the husband with his revolver in his hand. I held up my gun to *scare* him off and let me get away. He fired and missed me. I pulled off almost at the same instant, and down he dropped. I made away across the garden, and as I went I heard the window shut behind me. And that's all I know."

A cab had driven up while the American had been talking. Two uniformed policemen sat inside. Inspector Martin rose and *escorted* the prisoner outside. We stood at the window and watched the cab drive away.

The American, Abe Slaney, was *ultimately* condemned to life *imprisonment*. As for Mrs. Hilton Cubitt, I only know that I have heard she recovered entirely, and that she still, remains a *widow*, devoting her whole life to the care of the poor and to the *administration* of her husband's *estate*.

注释

brew [ˈbruː] *v.* 酿造,酝酿

odorous [ˈəudərəs] *adj.* 有气味的,臭的

security [siˈkjuəti] *n.* 有价证券

cue [kjuː] *n.* 暗示

expire [iksˈpaiə, eks-] *v.* 期满

analysis [əˈnælisis] *n.* 分析

association [əsəusiˈeiʃən] *n.* 交际,交往

faint [feint] *n.* 昏倒

appeal [əˈpiːl] *n.* 请求

justify [ˈdʒʌstifai] *v.* 证明…为正当

lodger [ˈlɔdʒə] *n.* 寄宿者

sample [ˈsæmpl] *n.* 标本,样品

indefinite [inˈdefinit] *adj.* 模糊的,不确定的

investigation [inˌvestiˈgeiʃən] *n.* 调查

weary [ˈwiəri] *v.* 疲倦

take the plunge 冒险尝试

inscription [inˈskripʃən] *n.* 题字

revolver [riˈvɔlvə] *n.* 左轮手枪

creeping [ˈkriːpiŋ] *adj.* 爬行的

intricate [ˈintrikit] *adj.* 错综复杂的

elaborate [iˈlæbərət] *adj.* 详细阐述的

calculation [ˌkælkjuˈleiʃən] *n.* 计算,考虑

enclose [inˈkləuz] *v.* 装入,围绕

dismay [disˈmei] *n.* 沮丧

bizarre [biˈzɑː] *adj.* 奇异的

lawn [lɔːn] *n.* 草坪

wax [wæks] *v.* 月亮渐满

cooperate [kəu'ɔpəreit] *v.* 合作

utmost ['ʌtməust] *adj.* 极度的

venture ['ventʃə] *v.* 冒险

conceivable [kən'siːvəbl] *adj.* 可想象的,可能的

arouse [ə'rəuz] *v.* 唤醒

disordered [dis'ɔːdəd] *adj.* 凌乱的

hastily ['heistili] *adv.* 慌忙地

bullet ['bulit] *n.* 子弹

instantaneous [ˌinstən'teinjəs] *adj.* 即刻的,瞬间的

fume [fjuːm] *n.* 烟,气体

masculine ['mɑːskjulin] *adj.* 男性的

peculiarly [pi'kjuːliəli] *adv.* 特别地

stable ['steibl] *n.* 马厩

dispatch [dis'pætʃ] *v.* 派遣

depart [di'pɑːt] *v.* 启程,离开

profitable ['prɔfitəbl] *adj.* 有利可图的,有益的

perceive [pə'siːv] *v.* 觉察

termination [ˌtəːmi'neiʃən] *n.* 终止

vacancy ['veikənsi] *n.* 空白,空缺

contraction [kən'trækʃən] *n.* 缩写

cable ['keibl] *v.* 发电报

persuasion [pə(ː)'sweiʒən] *n.* 劝告,说服

threat [θret] *n.* 恐吓,威胁

stride [straid] *v.* 大步行走

precaution [pri'kɔːʃən] *n.* 预防,警惕

wrist ['rist] *n.* 手腕,腕关节

blazing ['bleiziŋ] *adj.* 炽热的,强烈的

composure [kəm'pəuʒə] *n.* 镇静,沉着

The Adventure of The Dancing Men

pledge [pledʒ] *v.* 保证,使发誓

gang [gæŋ] *n.* (一)伙

suicide [ˌsjuisaid] *n.* 自杀

the Joint 监狱

bribe [braib] *v.* 贿赂

scare [skɛə] *v.* 威吓

escort [ˈeskɔt] *v.* 护送,陪同

ultimately [ˈʌltimətli] *adv.* 最后,终于

imprisonment [imˈprizənmənt] *n.* 关押

widow [ˈwidəu] *n.* 寡妇

administration [ədminisˈtreiʃən] *n.* 管理,经营

THE ADVENTURE OF THE BLUE CARBUNCLE

I had called upon my friend Sherlock Holmes upon the second morning after Christmas, with the *intention* of wishing him the *compliments* of the season. He was lounging upon the sofa in a purple dressing gown, making a study of a dirty hat which hung from the back of a wooden chair.

"I suppose," I remarked, "that, homely as it looks, this hat has some deadly story linked to it — that it is the clue which will guide you in the solution of some mystery and the punishment of some crime."

"No, no. No crime," said Sherlock Holmes, laughing. "You know Peterson, the *commissioner*?"

"Yes."

"It is to him that this trophy belongs."

"It is his hat."

"No, no; he found it. At about four o'clock on Christmas morning, Peterson, who, as you know, is a very honest fellow, was making his way homeward down Tottenham Court Road. In front of him he saw, in the gaslight, a tall man, walking with a slight *stagger*, and carrying a white goose slung over his shoulder. As he reached the corner of Goodge

Street, a row broke out between this stranger and a little group of roughs. One of the latter knocked off the man's hat, on which he raised his stick to defend himself and, swinging it over his head, smashed the shop window behind him. Peterson ran to help the man, but shocked at having broken the window, the stranger took to his heels, and *vanished amid* the *maze* of small sheets which lie at the back of Tottenham Court Road. The roughs had also fled at the appearance of Peterson, so that he was left in possession of the field of battle, and also of the spoils of victory in the shape of this *battered* hat and a Christmas goose."

"Which surely he restored to their owner?"

"My dear fellow, there lies the problem. It is true that 'For Mrs. Henry Baker' was printed upon a small card which was tied to the bird's left leg, and it is also true that the initials 'H. B. ' are written upon the lining of this hat; but as there are some hundreds of Henry Bakers in this city of ours, it is not easy to restore lost property to any one of them."

"What, then, did Peterson do?"

"He brought round both hat and goose to me on Christmas morning, knowing that even the smallest problems are of interest to me. Seeing as the goose would quickly go bad, I suggested that he take it home and eat it, while I try to discover the identity of the stranger. ”

“And what clue could you have as to his identity?”

“Only this hat. ”

“But you are joking. ”

“Here is my lens. You know my methods. ”

“Then, please tell me what it is that you can infer from this hat?”

He picked it up and gazed at it for a moment.

“That the man was highly *intellectual*, is of course obvious upon the face of it, and also that he was fairly well-to-do within the last three years, although he has now fallen upon bad days. He had foresight, but has less now than formerly, pointing to some evil influence, probably drink, at work upon him. This may account also for the obvious fact that his wife has ceased to love him. ”

“My dear Holmes. I have no doubt that I am very stupid, but I must confess that I am unable to follow you. For example, how did you *deduce* that this man was intellectual?”

For answer Holmes clapped the hat upon his head. It came right over the forehead and settled upon the bridge of his nose.

"A man with so large a brain must have something in it."

"The decline of his fortunes, then?"

"This hat is three years old. These flat brims curled at the edge came in then. It is a hat of the very best quality. If this man could afford to buy so expensive a hat three years ago, and has had no hat since, then he has assuredly gone down in the world."

"Well, that is clear enough, certainly. But how about the foresight?"

Sherlock Holmes laughed. "Here is the foresight," said he, putting his finger upon the little hat *securer*. "These are never sold upon hats. If this man ordered one, it is a sign of a certain amount of foresight, since he went out of his way to take this precaution against the wind. But since we see that he has broken the *elastic* and has not troubled to replace it, it is obvious that he has less foresight now than formerly, which is a distinct proof of a *weakening* nature."

"But his wife — you said that she had ceased to

love him. "

"This hat has not been brushed for weeks. When I see you, my dear Watson, with a week's *accumulation* of dust upon your hat, and when your wife allows you to go out in such a state, I shall fear that you also have been unfortunate enough to lose your wife's *affection*. "

"But he might be a *bachelor*. "

"No, he was bringing home the goose as a peace-offering to his wife. Remember the card upon the bird's leg. "

"Well, it is very *ingenious*," said I, laughing; "but since, as you said just now, there has been no crime *committed*, and no harm done save the loss of a goose, all this seems to be rather a waste of energy. "

Sherlock Holmes had opened his mouth to reply, when the door flew open, and Peterson, the Commissioner, rushed into the apartment with flushed cheeks and amazement on his face.

"The goose, Mr. Holmes!" he *gasped*. "See here, sir! See what my wife found in its stomach!" He held out his hand and displayed upon the center of the palm a *brilliantly* blue stone, which *twinkled* like an electric point in the dark hollow of his hand.

Sherlock Holmes sat up with a whistle.

"By Jove, Peterson! That's no mere precious stone."

"Not the Countess of Morcar's blue carbuncle!" I cried.

"Precisely so. I ought to know its size and shape, seeing that I have read the advertisement about it in The Times every day lately. It is absolutely unique, and its value can only be guessed at."

"It was lost, if I remember correctly, at the Hotel Cosmopolitan," I remarked.

"Precisely so, just five days ago. John Horner, a *plumber*, was accused of having *abstracted* it from the lady's jewelcase. I have some account of the matter here, I believe." He rummaged amid his newspapers, glancing over the dates, until at last he smoothed one out, doubled it over, and read the following paragraph:

"Hotel Cosmopolitan Jewel Robbery. John Horner, 26, plumber, was brought up upon the charge of having abstracted from the jewel-case of the Countess of Morcar the valuable jewel known as the blue carbuncle. James Ryder, upper-*attendant* at the hotel, gave his evidence to the effect that he had shown Horner up to the dressing room of the Countess upon the day of the robbery in order that he might repair a loose bar in her room's *grate*. He had remained with Horner some little time, but had finally been called away. On returning, he found that Horner had disappeared, and that the *bureau* had been forced open. Ryder instantly gave the alarm, and Horner was *captured* the same evening; but the stone could not be found either upon his person or in his rooms.

"Horner, who was known to have a previous *conviction* for robbery, *protested* his innocence in the strongest terms. His case, seeming rather clear cut, is awaiting a *verdict*, expected to be passed this week."

"You see, Watson, our little *deductions* regarding this hat have suddenly assumed a much more important and less innocent aspect. So now we must set ourselves very seriously to finding the owner of this hat in order to see what part he has played in this little mystery. We'll do this by placing an advertisement in all the evening papers. It's likely that he'll want to recover both his hat and bird. Here you are, Peterson," he said, handing the commissioner a paper with the ad he wished to run. "Take this to the advertising agency and have this put in the evening papers. "

"Very well, sir. And this stone?"

"Ah, yes, I shall keep the stone. Thank you. And, I say, Peterson, just buy a goose on your way back and leave it here with me, for we must have one to give to this gentleman in place of the one which your family is now devouring. "

When the commissioner had gone, I also prepared to leave and finish my evening rounds.

"Come back around six o'clock," said Holmes. "That's the time I indicated in the advertisement for Henry Baker to come and see about his things. "

"I'll be here," I replied, taking my leave.

I had been delayed at a case, and it was a little after half-past six when I found myself in Baker Street once more. As I approached the house I saw a tall man standing in Holmes's *doorway*. Just as I arrived the door was opened, and we were shown up together to Holmes's room.

"Mr. Henry Baker, I believe," said he, rising from his armchair and greeting his visitor with the easy air of friendliness which he could so readily assume. "Ah, Watson, you have just come at the right time. Is that your hat, Mr. Baker?"

"Yes, sir, that is undoubtedly my hat."

He was a large man with rounded shoulders, a massive head, and a broad, *intelligent* face. A touch of red in nose and cheeks, with a slight shaking of his *extended* hand, recalled Holmes's guess as to his drinking habits.

"By the way, about the bird, we were *compelled* to eat it," said Holmes.

"To eat it!" Our visitor half rose from his chair in his excitement.

"Yes, it would have been of no use to anyone had we not done so. But I presume that this other goose here, will answer your purpose equally well?"

"Oh, certainly, certainly," answered Mr. Baker, who seeing another bird on the table, sighed in relief.

"Of Course, we still have the feathers, legs, crop, and so on of your own bird, so if you wish —" The man burst into a hearty laugh.

"They might be useful to me as relics of my adventure," said he, "but beyond that I can hardly see what use they would be to me. No, sir, I think that, with your permission, I will confine my attentions to the excellent bird which I perceive here."

Sherlock Holmes glanced sharply across at me with a slight shrug of his shoulders.

"There is your hat, then, and there your bird," said he. "By the way, would it bore you to tell me where you got the other one from?"

"No at all, sir," said Baker, who had risen and tucked his newly gained property under his arm.

"Windigate, the host at the Alpha Inn, started a goose club, the members of which all received a Christmas goose."

And then, with a *comical arrogance* of manner, he bowed solemnly to both of us and strode off upon his way.

"So much for Mr. Henry Baker," said Holmes when he had closed the door behind him. "It is quite certain that he knows nothing whatever about the matter. Now I suggest that we follow up this clue while it is still hot."

"By all means."

In a quarter of an hour we were in Bloomsbury at the Alpha Inn. Holmes pushed open the door of the private bar and ordered two glasses of beer from the landlord.

"Your beer should be excellent if it is as good as your geese," said he.

"My geese !" The man seemed surprised.

"Yes. I was speaking only half an hour ago to Mr. Henry Baker, who was a member of your goose club."

"Ah, yes. But you see, sir, them's not our geese."

"Indeed! Whose, then?"

"Well, I got the two dozen from a salesman named Breckenridge in Covent Garden."

"Ah! Well, here's your good health, landlord, and *prosperity* to your house. Goodnight."

"Now for Mr. Breckenridge," he continued, buttoning up his coat as we came out into the frosty air. "Faces to the south, then, and quick march!"

We passed through a *zigzag* of *slums* to Covent Garden Market. One of the largest stalls bore the name of Breckenridge upon it, and the owner, a horsy-looking man, with a sharp face and trim *sideburns*, was helping a boy to put up the *shutters*.

"Good evening. It's a cold night," said Holmes.

The salesman nodded and shot a questioning glance at my companion.

"Sold out of geese, I see," continued Holmes, pointing at the bare slabs of marble. "I was recommended to you by the landlord of Alpha."

"Oh, yes; I sent him a couple of dozen."

"Now where did you get them from?"

To my surprise the question *provoked* a burst of anger from the salesman.

"Now, then, mister," said he, with his head cocked and his arms crossed, "what are you driving at? Let's have it straight, now."

"Oh, it is a matter of no importance; but I don't know why you should be so warm over such a trifle."

"Warm! You'd be as warm, maybe, if you were as pestered as I am. One would think they were the only geese in the world, to hear the *fuss* that is made over them."

"Well, if you won't tell us the bet is off, that is all. I have five pounds on it that the bird I ate is country bred."

"Well, then, you've lost, for it's town bred," *snapped* the salesman.

"It's nothing of the kind."

"Do you think you know more about birds than I, who have handled them ever since I was a kid? I'll bet you now those birds were town bred."

"It's merely taking your money, for I know that I am right. But let's bet anyhow."

The salesman chuckled *grimly*. "Bring me the books, Bill," said he.

The small boy brought round a small thin volume and a great *greasy*-backed one, laying them out together beneath the hanging lamp.

"Now then, here is a list of the people I get my birds from. Now, look at that third name. 'Mrs. Oakshott, 117, Brixton Road.' Now look at the next column: 'December 22nd. Twenty-four geese to Alpha Inn.'"

Sherlock Holmes drew a *sovereign* from his pocket and threw it down upon the slab, turning away with the air of a man whose *disgust* is too deep for words. A few yards off he stopped under a lamp and laughed in the hearty, noiseless fashion, which was peculiar to him.

"I knew he wouldn't be able to refuse a bet. Well, Watson, we are, I fancy, nearing the end of our quest, and the only point which remains to be determined is whether we should go on to this Mrs. Oakshott tonight, or whether we should reserve it for. . ."

His remarks were suddenly cut short by a loud argument which broke out from the stall we had just left. Turning round we saw a little rat-faced fellow standing near Breckenridge's stall, while the salesman shook his fist at him.

"If you come pestering me any more with your talk about geese, I'll set the dog at you. You bring Mrs. Oakshott here and I'll answer her, but what have you to do with it? Get out of here!"

He rushed fiercely forward, and the *inquirer* ran away into the darkness.

"Ha! This may save us a visit to Brixton Road," whispered Holmes.

Striding through the scattered *knots* of people, my companion speedily *overtook* the little man and touched him upon the shoulder. He sprang round, looking quite frightened.

"What do you want?" he asked in a shaky voice.

"My name is Sherlock Holmes. I *overheard* your conversation back there, and I believe that I can help you to track down the goose you're after."

"Oh, sir, you are the very man whom I have longed to meet," cried the little fellow with outstretched hands and quivering fingers.

Sherlock Holmes *hailed* a carriage, which was passing. "In that case we had better discuss it in a comfortable room rather than in this wind-swept marketplace," said he. "But please tell me, before we go farther, who it is that I have the pleasure of assisting."

"My name is James Ryder."

"Ah! Head attendant at the Hotel Cosmopolitan. Please step into the cab, and I shall soon be able to tell you everything which you would wish to know."

The little man nervously stepped into the cab, and in half an hour we were back in the sitting room at Baker Street.

"Here we are!" said Holmes cheerily as we filed into the room. "You look cold, Mr. Ryder. Please take the seat next to the fire. Now, then! You want to know what became of that goose?"

"Yes, sir. Can you tell me where it went to?"

"It came here."

"Here?"

"Yes, and a most remarkable bird it proved. It laid an egg after it was dead — the brightest little blue egg that ever was seen. I have it here in my museum."

Our visitor *staggered* to his feet and stared as Holmes *unlocked* his *strongbox* and held up the blue carbuncle.

"The game's up, Ryder," said Holmes quietly. "Help him, Watson. He looks as though he might faint."

I helped the man back into his chair and gave him a *sip* of *brandy*, which helped to calm his wild eyes.

"It seems to me, Ryder, that there is the making of a very pretty villain in you. You knew that this man Horner, the plumber, had been arrested for theft before, and that suspicion would rest the more readily upon him. Thus, you had him sent for to make repairs to the lady's room. Then, when he had left, you *rifled* the jewelcase, raised the alarm, and had this unfortunate man taken to jail. You then—"

Ryder threw himself down suddenly upon the rug and *clutched* at my companion's knees.

"For God's sake, have mercy!" he *shrieked*. "Think of my father and mother! I never went wrong before! I never will again. I swear it. Oh, don't bring it into court!"

"Get back into your chair!" said Holmes *sternly*. "It is very well to beg and *crawl* now, but you thought little enough of this poor Horner in the *dock* for a crime of which he knew nothing."

"I will fly, Mr. Holmes. I will leave the country, sir. Then the charge against him will break down."

"Hm! We will talk about that. And now let us hear a true account of the next act. Tell us the truth, for there lies your only hope of safety."

Ryder passed his tongue over his dry lips. "I will tell you it just as it happened, sir. When Horner had been taken away, it seemed to me that it would be best to get away with the stone at once, there was no place about the hotel where the jewel would be safe. I made for my sister's house. She had married a man named Oakshott, and lived in Brixton Road, where she raised geese for the market. At her home, I went to the *backyard* to hide and try to calm down. Unsure whether I would be suspected or not, I feared the police and thought I might at any moment be seized and searched, and there would be the stone in my pocket. Seeing all the geese around me, an idea came into my head.

"My sister had intended to give me whatever goose I liked for a Christmas gift. I decided to choose that goose now, and catching a quite fat one, I pried open its bill and *thrust* the stone down its throat as far as my finger could reach. The bird gave a gulp, and cried and *flapped* about, joining the rest of geese. My sister came out at that moment to see what was the matter. In turning to face her, I lost sight of my goose." 'Have you chosen your goose?' my sister asked. Remembering my goose had a black bar across its tail, I found the goose with this mark and pointed it out to her. It was then killed and *plucked* and I took it home. Much to my horror, however, the jewel was not inside the goose. I then ran back to my sisters, only to find that she had sold them all to a man named Breckenridge at the market. When I asked if any had had a black bar across the tail, she told me that one did indeed have it.

"Well, then I ran off as hard as my feet would carry me to this man Breckenridge; but he had sold the lot at once, and not one word would he tell me as to where they had gone. My sister thinks that I am going mad. Sometimes I think that I am myself. God help me!"

He burst into tears, with his face buried in his hands.

There was a long silence, broken only by his heavy breathing, and by the measured tapping of Sherlock Holmes's fingers upon the edge of the table. Then my friend rose and threw open the door.

"Get out!" said he.

"What, sir! Oh, Heaven bless you!"

"No more words. Get out!"

And no more words were needed. There was a rush, a clatter upon the stairs, the bang of a door, and the crisp rattle of running footfalls from the street.

"If Horner were in danger it would be another thing," said Holmes, "but this fellow will not appear against him, and the case must *collapse*. This fellow won't go wrong again; he is too terribly frightened. Send him to jail now, and you make him a criminal for life. Besides, it is the season of forgiveness. Chance has put in our way a most singular and unusual problem, and its solution is its own reward."

注释

intention [in'tenʃən] *n.* 意图

The Adventure of The Blue Carbuncle

compliment [ˈkɔmplimənt] *n.* 称赞,恭维

commissioner [kəˈmiʃənə] *n.* 专员,委员

stagger [ˈstæɡə] *n.* 蹒跚,踉跄

vanish [ˈvæniʃ] *v.* 消失

amid [əˈmid] *prep.* 在…中

maze [meiz] *n.* 曲径,迷宫

battered [ˈbætəd] *adj.* 打扁了的

intellectual [ˌintiˈlektjuəl] *adj.* 有智力的

cease [si:s] *v.* 停止

deduce [diˈdju:s] *v.* 推论,演绎出

securer [siˈkjuərə] *n.* 保卫者

elastic [iˈlæstik] *adj.* 有弹性的

weakening [ˌwi:kəniŋ] *n.* 弱化

accumulation [əkju:mjuˈleiʃ(ə)n] *n.* 积聚物

affection [əˈfekʃən] *n.* 爱情

bachelor [ˈbætʃələ] *n.* 单身汉

ingenious [inˈdʒi:njəs] *adj.* 机灵的,有独创性的

commit [kəˈmit] *v.* 犯错误

gasp [ɡɑ:sp] *v.* 气喘吁吁地说

brilliantly [ˈbriljəntli] *adv.* 光亮地,灿烂地

twinkle [ˈtwiŋkl] *v.* 闪耀

plumber [ˈplʌmbə] *n.* 水管工人

abstract [ˈæbstrækt] *v.* 偷

attendant [əˈtendənt] *n.* 服务员

grate [ɡreit] *n.* 壁炉

bureau [bjuəˈrəu, ˈbjuərəu] *n.* 办公桌,衣柜,(美)梳妆台

capture [ˈkæptʃə] *v.* 俘获

conviction [kənˈvikʃən] *n.* 定罪

protest [prəˈtest] *v.* 断言抗议

verdict [ˈvə:dikt] *n.* 判决

deduction [di'dʌkʃən] *n.* 推论，演绎

doorway ['dɔ:wei] *n.* 门口

intelligent [in'telidʒənt] *adj.* 聪明的

extended [iks'tendid] *adj.* 伸出的

compel [kəm'pel] *v.* 强迫，迫使

comical ['kɔmik(ə)l] *adj.* 滑稽的，好笑的

arrogance ['ærəgəns] *n.* 傲慢态度

prosperity [prɔs'periti] *n.* 繁荣

zigzag ['zigzæg] *adj.* 曲折的

slum [slʌm] *n.* 贫民区

sideburns ['saidbə:n] *n.* 连鬓胡子

shutter ['ʃʌtə] *n.* 遮蔽物，窗板

provoke [prə'vəuk] *v.* 激怒，惹起

fuss [fʌs] *n.* 大惊小怪

snap [snæp] *v.* 快速地说

grimly ['grimli] *adv.* 冷酷地

greasy ['gri:si, 'gri:zi] *adj.* 油污的

sovereign ['sɔvrin] *n.* (英国从前的)一镑金币

disgust [dis'gʌst] *n.* 厌恶

inquirer [in'kwaiərə] *n.* 调查者，询问的人

knot [nɔt] *n.* 一小群人

overtake [,əuvə'teik] *v.* 追上

overhear [,əuvə'hiə] *v.* 无意中听到

hail [heil] *v.* 招呼

stagger ['stægə] *v.* 摇摆，蹒跚

unlock ['ʌn'lɔk] *v.* 开启

strongbox ['strɔŋbɔks] *n.* 保险箱

sip [sip] *n.* 一小口

brandy ['brændi] *n.* 白兰地酒

rifle ['raifl] *v.* 掠夺

The Adventure of The Blue Carbuncle

rug [rʌg] *n.* 地毯

clutch [klʌtʃ] *v.* 抓住

shriek [ʃri:k] *v.* 尖声喊叫

sternly [stə:nli] *adv.* 严厉地

crawl [krɔ:l] *v.* （由于害怕或讨厌）使人毛发直竖

dock [dɔk] *n.* 被告席

backyard [bækjɑ:d] *n.* 后院

thrust [θrʌst] *v.* 力推，插入

flap [flæp] *v.* 拍打，鼓翼而飞

pluck [plʌk] *v.* 拔毛

collapse [kəlæps] *v.* 崩溃，失败

THE ADVENTURE OF THE SECOND STAIN

I had intended "The Adventure of the Abbey Grange" to be the last of those exploits of my friend, Mr. Sherlock Holmes, which I should ever communicate to the public. The reason for this *resolution* lay in the *reluctance* which Mr. Holmes has shown to the continued publication of his experiences. Since he has definitely retired from London and betaken himself to study and bee farming on the Sussex Downs, fame has become hateful to him. It was only upon my representing to him that I had given a promise that "The Adventure of the Second Stain" should be published when the times were ripe, and pointing out to him that it is only *appropriate* that this long series of *episodes* should *culminate* in the most important international case which he has ever been called upon to handle, that I at last succeeded in obtaining his *consent* that a carefully guarded account of the incident should at last be laid before the public.

It was, then, in a year, and even in a *decade*, that shall be nameless, that upon one Tuesday morning in autumn we found two visitors of European fame within the walls of our *humble* room in Baker Street.

One was none other than Lord Bellinger, twice Premier of Britain. The other was the *Honorable* Trelawney Hope, Secretary for European Affairs, and the most rising statesman in the country. They sat side by side upon our paper-littered sofa, and it was easy to see from their worn and anxious faces that it was business of the most pressing importance which had brought them.

"When I discovered my loss, Mr. Holmes, which was at eight o'clock this morning, I at once informed the Prime Minister," said Trelawney Hope. "It was at his suggestion that we have both come to you."

"Have you informed the police?"

"No, sir. To inform the police must, in the long run, mean to inform the public. This is what we particularly desire to avoid."

"And why, sir?"

"Because the document in question is of such immense importance that its publication might very easily lead to European *complications* of the utmost moment. It is not too much to say that peace or war may hang upon the issue."

"I understand. Now, Mr. Trelawney Hope, I

should be much obliged if you would tell me exactly the circumstances under which this document disappeared. "

"That can be done in a very few words, Mr. Holmes. The letter — for it was a letter from a foreign ruler — was received six days ago. It was of such importance that I have never left it in my safe, but have taken it across each evening to my house in Whitehall Terrace, and kept it in my bedroom in a locked *dispatch* box. It was there last night. Of that I am certain. I actually opened the box while I was dressing for dinner and saw the document inside. This morning it was gone. My wife and I are both light sleepers, it's impossible that someone could have come in at night. "

"What time did you dine?"

"Half-past seven. "

"How long was it before you went to bed?"

"My wife had gone to the theatre. I waited up for her. It was half-past eleven before we went to our room. "

"Then for four hours the dispatch box had lain unguarded?"

"No one is ever permitted to enter that room save

the maid in the morning, and my servant. They are both loyal servants who have been with us for some time."

"Who knew of the existence of that letter?"

"No one in the house."

"Surely your wife knew"

"No, sir. I had said nothing to my wife until I missed the paper this morning."

"Who is there in England who did know of the existence of this letter?"

"Each member of the Cabinet was informed of it yesterday, but the *pledge* of secrecy which attends every Cabinet meeting was increased by the *solemn* warning which was given by the Prime Minister. Besides the members of the Cabinet there are two, or possibly three, departmental officials who know of the letter. No one else in England, Mr. Holmes, I assure you."

"But abroad?"

"I believe that no one abroad has seen it save the man who wrote it."

Holmes considered for some little time.

"Now, sir, I must ask you more particularly what this document is, and why its disappearance should have such momentous *consequences?*"

"The envelope is a long, thin one of pale blue color. There is a seal of red *wax* stamped..."

"I fear, sir," said Holmes, "that, I must know what the letter was?"

"That is a State secret of the utmost importance, and I fear that I cannot tell you, nor do I see that it is necessary."

Sherlock Holmes rose with a smile.

"You are two of the most busy men in the country," said he, "and in my own small way I have also a good many calls upon me. I regret exceedingly that I cannot help you in this matter, and any *continuation* of this interview would be a waste of time."

The Premier sprang to his feet fiercely, "I am not *accustomed*, sir," he began, but mastered his anger and *resumed* his seat. For a minute or more we all sat in silence. Then the old statesman shrugged his shoulders.

"We must accept your terms, Mr. Holmes. And we tell you, relying entirely upon your honor and that of your colleague, Dr. Watson. I may appeal to your *patriotism* also, for I could not imagine a greater *misfortune* for the country than that this affair should come out. "

"You may safely trust us. "

"The letter, then, is from a certain foreign leader who has been ruffled by some recent colonial developments of this country. It has been written hurriedly and upon his own responsibility entirely, and certain phrases in it are of so *provocative* a character, that its publication would undoubtedly lead to a most dangerous state of feeling in this country. There would be such an *uproar*, sir, that I do not hesitate to say that within a week of the publication of that letter this country would be involved in a great war. "

Holmes wrote a name upon a slip of paper and handed it to the Premier.

"Exactly. It was he," said the Premier.

"Perhaps he desires the publication of the letter. "

"No, sir. It would be a greater blow to him and to his country than to us if this letter were to come out. "

"If this is so, whose interest is it that the letter should come out?"

"There, Mr. Holmes, you take me into regions of high international politics. The whole of Europe is an armed camp. There is a double league, which makes a fair balance of military power. Great Britain holds the scales. If Britain were driven into war with one side, it would assure the *superiority* of the other, whether they joined in the war or not. Do you follow?"

"Very clearly. It is then the interest of the enemies of this leader to *secure* and publish this letter, so as to make a *breach* between his country and ours?"

"Yes, sir. Now you are in full possession of the facts. What course do you recommend?"

Holmes shook his head mournfully.

"Considering that it could only have been taken yesterday evening between seven thirty and eleven thirty, and understanding that there is no entrance from without, and that from within no one could go up unobserved, it must be somebody in the house who has taken it. Now then, to whom would the thief take it? To one of several international spies and secret agents, whose names are *tolerably* familiar to me. There are three who may be said to be the heads of their profession. I will begin my research by going round and finding if each of them is at his post. If one is missing — especially if he has disappeared since last night — we will have some indication as to where the document has gone. "

"I believe you are right, Mr. Holmes," said Lord Bellinger. "Meanwhile, Hope, we cannot neglect all our other duties on account of this one misfortune. Should there be any fresh developments during the day we shall communicate with you, and you will no doubt let us know the results of your own inquiries. "

The two statesmen bowed and walked gravely from the room.

When our visitors had departed, Holmes lit his pipe in silence and sat for some time lost in the deepest thought. I had opened the morning paper and was *immersed* in a *sensational* crime, which had occurred in London the night before, when my friend gave an exclamation and sprang to his feet.

"Yes," said he, "it is just possible that the letter has not yet passed out of the spy's hands. After all, it is a question of money with these fellows, and I have the British treasury behind me. If it's on the market, I'll buy it. It is conceivable that the fellow might hold it back to see what *bids* come from this side before he tries his luck on the other. There are

only those three capable of playing so bold a game —
there are Oberstein, La Rothiere, and Eduardo Lucas. I will see each of them. "

I glanced at my morning paper.

"Eduardo Lucas of Godolphin Street?"

"Yes. "

"You will not see him. "

"Why not?"

"He was murdered in his house last night. "

My friend stared in amazement, and then snatched
the paper from my hands, which read:

"MURDER IN WESTMINSTER — A crime of
mysterious character was committed last night at 16
Godolphin Street. Mr. Eduardo Lucas, well known
in society on account of his charming *personality*,
was found dead by police officer, Barrett, as he was
passing along Godolphin Street and observed that the
door of No. 16 was a little open. The room in which
Mr. Lucas was found was in a state of wild disorder,
the furniture being all swept to one side, and one
chair lying on its back in the center. The victim had
been stabbed to the heart and must have died instantly. The knife with which the crime had been committed was a *curved* Indian dagger, plucked down from a

trophy of Oriental arms which adorned one of the walls. Robbery does not appear to have been the motive of the crime, for there had been no attempt to remove the valuable contents of the room. "

"Well, Watson, what do you make of this?" asked Holmes, after a long pause.

"It is an amazing *coincidence*. "

"The odds are enormous against its being coincidence. No, my dear Watson, the two events are connected — must be connected. It is for us to find the connection. Hello! What have we here?"

Mrs. Hudson, Holmes's servant, had appeared with a lady's card upon her tray.

Holmes glanced at it, raised his eyebrows, and handed it over to me.

"Ask Lady Hilda Trelawney Hope if she will be kind enough to step up, " said he.

A moment later our modest apartment, already so *distinguished* that morning, was further honored by the entrance of the loveliest woman in London. Yet her beauty was not what first sprang to the eye this meeting, for her *features* were clearly *overtaken* by emotion and concern.

"Has my husband been here, Mr. Holmes?"

"Yes, madam."

"Mr. Holmes. I am aware that there was a most deplorable *occurrence* in our house last night. I know that a paper has disappeared. But because the matter is political my husband refuses to take me into his complete confidence. Now it is essential — essential, I say — that I should thoroughly understand it. I assure you that his interests, if he would only see it, would be best served by taking me into his complete confidence. What was this paper which was stolen?"

"Madam, what you ask me is really impossible. It is him whom you must ask."

"I have asked him. I come to you as a last resource. But without your telling me anything definite, Mr. Holmes, you may do a great service if you would *enlighten* me on one point."

"What is it, madam?"

"Is my husband's political career likely to suffer through this incident?"

"Well, madam, unless it is set right it may certainly have a very unfortunate effect."

"Ah!" She drew in her breath sharply as one whose doubts are *resolved*.

"And the public consequences which might arise

from the loss of this document?"

"There again you ask me more than I can possibly answer."

"Then I will take up no more of your time. I only ask that you will say nothing to anyone of my visit."

She looked back at us from the door, and I had a last impression of that beautiful *haunted* face, the *startled* eyes, and the drawn mouth. Then she was gone.

"Now, Watson. What would you say was the fair lady's game? What did she really want?"

"She was certainly much moved."

"Yes. Quite odd. And yet the motives of women are always so mysterious. Good morning, Watson."

"You are off?"

"Yes, I will while away the morning at Godolphin Street. With Eduardo Lucas lies the solution to our problem, though I must admit that I have not any idea as to what form it may take. Stay on guard, my good Watson, and receive any fresh visitors. I'll join you at lunch if I am able."

All that day and the next, and the next, Holmes was in a quiet and rather gloomy mood. It was evident to me that things were not going well with him or his quest. He would say nothing of the case. I learned of new developments from reading the newspapers. According to them, Eduardo Lucas's papers showed him to have been on intimate terms with the leading politicians of several countries. But nothing sensational was discovered among the documents which filled his drawers. His habits were regular, his conduct inoffensive. His death was an absolute mystery and likely to remain so.

Thus for three mornings the mystery remained, so far as I could follow it in the papers. Upon the fourth day there appeared in the papers news of a long telegram from Paris which seemed to solve the whole question:

"A discovery has just been made by the Parisian police which raises the veil which hung round the tragic death of Mr. Eduardo Lucas. Yesterday a lady, who has been known as Madame Henri Fournaye, was reported to the *authorities* by her servants as being *insane*. An examination showed she had indeed developed *insanity* of a dangerous and *permanent* form. On inquiry, the police have discovered that Madame Fournaye returned from a journey to London on Tuesday last, and there is evidence to connect her with the crime at Westminster. A comparison of photographs has proved conclusively that Mr. Henri Fournaye and Eduardo Lucas were really one and the same person.

Madame Fournaye is of an extremely excitable nature, and has suffered in the past from attacks of jealousy which have amounted to frenzy. It is believed that it was in one of these that she committed the terrible crime which has caused such a *sensation* in London. At present she is unable to give any coherent account of the past, and the doctors hold out no hopes of the *reestablishment* of her reason. There is evidence that a woman, who might have been Madame Fournaye, was seen for some hours upon Monday night watching the house in Godolphin Street. "

"What do you think of that, Holmes?" I had read the account aloud to him, while he finished his breakfast. "Surely it is final as regards the man's death. "

"The man's death is a mere incident — a *trivial* episode — in comparison with our real task, which is to trace this document and save a European *catastrophe*. Only one important thing has happened in the last three days, and that is that nothing has happened. Why has the document not been sent out? Did Lucas's mad wife carry it off with her? If so, how could I search for it without the French police having their *suspicions* aroused? It is a case, my dear Watson, where the law is as dangerous to us as the criminals are. Ah, here is my latest from the front! "

He glanced hurriedly at the note which had been handed in.

"Excellent! Lestrade seems to have observed something of interest. Put on your hat, Watson, and we will *stroll* down together to Westminster. "

At the scene of the crime, the room in which the murder took place showed no evidence of what had occurred except an ugly, irregular stain upon the carpet in the center of the room. Over the fireplace was a magnificent trophy of weapons, one of which had been used on that tragic night.

"Seen the Paris news?" asked Lestrade.

Holmes nodded.

"Our French friends seem to have touched the spot this time," Lestrade continued. "It seems there was a bit of a struggle, for these chairs were all swept over to one side, and he had a knife in his hand as if he had tried to hold her off with it. We've got it all clear as if we had seen it. "

Holmes raised his eyebrows.

"And yet you have sent for me?"

"Ah, yes, that's another matter — a mere trifle. This morning, as the man was buried and the investigation over — so far as this room is concerned — we thought we could tidy up a bit. This carpet, you see, is not fastened down, only just laid there. We had occasion to raise it. You see that stain on the carpet? Well, a great deal must have soaked through, must it not?"

"Undoubtedly it must. "

"Well, you will be surprised to hear that there is no stain on the white woodwork to correspond. "

"And how is that?"

"Well, I'll show you the explanation. There is a second stain, but it does not correspond with the other. See for yourself. " As he spoke he turned over another *portion* of the carpet, and there, sure enough, was a great crimson *spill* upon the square white facing of the old-fashioned floor. "What do you make of that, Mr. Holmes?"

"Why, it is simple enough. The carpet has been turned round. "

"That's clear enough, for the *stains* lie above each other if you lay it over this way. But what I want to know is who shifted the carpet, and why?"

I could see from Holmes's rigid face that he was *vibrating* with *inward* excitement.

"Look here, Lestrade," said he, "has that guard in the passage been in charge of the place all the time?"

"Yes, he has."

"Well, take my advice. You take him into the back room and ask him how he dared to admit people and leave them alone in this room. Don't ask him if he has done it. Take it for granted. Tell him you know someone has been here. Press him. Tell him that a full confession is his only chance of forgiveness. Do exactly what I tell you!"

Lestrade immediately *darted* into the hall, and a few moments later his *bullying* voice sounded from the back room.

"Now, Watson, now!" cried Holmes with frenzied eagerness. Holmes tore the rug from the floor, and in an instant, was down on his hands and knees *clawing* at each of the squares of wood beneath it. One turned sideways as he dug his nails into the edge of it. It *hinged* back like the lid of a box. A small black *cavity* opened beneath it. Holmes *plunged* his eager hand into it and drew it out with a bitter snarl of anger and disappointment. It was empty.

"Quick, Watson, quick! Get it back again!"

The wooden lid was replaced, and the rug had only just been drawn straight when Lestrade's voice was heard in the passage. He found Holmes leaning calmly against the wall, *resigned* and patient.

"Well, he has *confessed*, all right," said Lestrade. "Come in here, MacPherson. Let these gentlemen hear of your most inexcusable conduct."

The guard came *shamefacedly* into the room.

"I meant no harm, sir. A young, respectable woman came to the door last evening — mistook the house, she did. And then we got talking. She said she'd read about the crime that had happened here and wondered if she might see where it was done. I saw no harm in letting her have a peep. When she saw that mark on the carpet, down she dropped on the floor, and lay as if she were dead. I ran to the back and got some water, but I could not bring her to. Then I went round the corner to the Ivy Plant for some brandy, and by the time I had brought it back the young woman had recovered and was off. "

"How about moving that rug?"

"Well, sir, it was a bit out of place when I came back. You see, she fell on it and it lies on a *polished* floor with nothing to keep it in place. I straightened it out afterwards."

"It's a lesson to you that you can't deceive me, Constable MacPherson," said Lestrade, with dignity. "I'm sorry to have called you down over such a petty business, Mr. Holmes, but I thought the second stain would interest you."

"Certainly, it was most interesting. Has this woman only been here once, officer?"

"Yes, sir, only once."

"Tall? Handsome?"

"Yes, sir, she was a well-grown young woman. I suppose you might say she was handsome."

"What time was it?"

"It was just growing dusk at the time. They were lighting the lamps as I came back with the brandy."

"Very good," said Holmes. "Come, Watson, I think that we have more important work elsewhere."

As we left the house Lestrade remained in the

front room, while the *repentant* guard opened the door to let us out. Holmes turned on the step and held up something in his hand. The guard stared *intently*.

"Good Lord, sir!" he cried, with amazement on his face. Holmes put his finger on his lips, replaced his hand in his breast pocket, and burst out laughing as we turned down the street.

"Excellent!" said he.

"Come, friend Watson, the curtain rings up for the last act. You will be relieved to hear that there will be no war, that the Honorable Trelawney Hope will suffer no *setback* in his brilliant career, that the *indiscreet* foreign leader will receive no punishment for his indiscretion, that the Prime Minister will have no European complication to deal with, and that with a little tact and *management* upon our part nobody will be a penny the worse for what might have been a very ugly incident. "

"You have solved it!" I cried.

"Hardly that, Watson. There are some points which are as dark as ever. But we have so much that it will be our own fault if we cannot get the rest. We will go straight to Whitehall Terrace and bring the matter to a head."

When we arrived at the *residence* of the European Secretary it was for Lady Hilda Trelawney Hope that Sherlock Holmes *inquired*. We were shown into the morning room.

"Mr. Holmes!" said the lady, and her face was pink with *indignation*. "I desired to keep my visit to you a secret. And yet you *compromise* me by coming here and so showing that there are business relations between us."

"Unfortunately, madam, I had no possible *alternative*. I know of your visit to Eduardo Lucas, of your giving him this document, of your ingenious return to the room last night, and of the manner in which you took the letter from the hiding-place under the carpet."

She stared at him with an ashen face and gulped twice before she could speak.

"You are mad, Mr. Holmes — you are mad!" she cried, at last.

He drew a small piece of cardboard from his pocket. It was the face of a woman cut out of a portrait.

"I have carried this because I thought it might be

useful," said he. "The policeman has recognized it."

She gave a gasp, and her head dropped back in the chair.

"Come, Lady Hilda. You have the letter. The matter may still be *adjusted*. I have no desire to bring trouble to you. My duty ends when I have returned the lost letter to your husband. Take my advice and be frank with me. It is your only chance."

Her courage was admirable. Even now she would not own defeat.

"I tell you again, Mr. Holmes, that you are under some absurd illusion."

Holmes rose from his chair.

"I am sorry for you, Lady Hilda. I have done my best for you. I can see that it is all in vain."

He rang the bell. The servant entered.

"Is Mr. Trelawney Hope at home?"

"He will be home, sir, in a quarter of an hour."

"Very good, I shall wait."

The servant had hardly closed the door behind him when Lady Hilda was down on her knees at Holmes's feet, her hands outstretched, her beautiful face wet with tears.

"Oh, spare me, Mr. Holmes! Spare me!" she

pleaded. "For heaven's sake, don't tell him! I love him so! I would not bring one shadow on his life, and this I know would break his noble heart."

Holmes raised the lady. "I am thankful, madam, that you have come to your senses even at this last moment! Where is the letter?"

She darted across to a writing desk, unlocked it, and drew out a long blue envelope.

"Here it is, Mr. Holmes!"

"Quick! Where is the dispatch box?"

"Still in his bedroom."

"What *a stroke of luck*! Bring it here, madam!" A moment later she had appeared with a red, flat box in her hand.

"How did you open it before? You have a duplicate key? Yes, of course you have. Open it!"

From out of her *bosom* Lady Hilda had drawn a small key. The box flew open. It was *stuffed* with papers. Holmes thrust the blue envelope deep down into the heart of them. The box was shut, locked, and returned to the bedroom.

"Now we are ready for him," said Holmes. "We have still ten minutes. I am going far to screen you, Lady Hilda. In return you will spend the time in telling me frankly the real meaning of this extraordinary affair."

"Mr. Holmes, I will tell you everything," cried the lady. It was a letter of mine, Mr. Holmes, an indiscreet letter written before my marriage — a foolish letter, a letter of an *impulsive*, loving girl. Had my husband read that letter his confidence would have been forever destroyed. I had thought that the whole matter was forgotten. Then at last I heard from this man, Lucas, that it had passed into his hands, and that he would lay it before my husband. I begged his mercy. He said that he would return my letter if I would bring him a certain document which he described in my husband's dispatch box. He had some spy in the office who had told him of its existence. He assured me that no harm could come to my husband. So, I did it, Mr. Holmes! I took an impression of his key. This man, Lucas, furnished a duplicate. I opened his dispatch box, took the paper, and *conveyed* it to Godolphin Street."

"What happened there, madam?"

"I delivered the document. I remember that there was a woman outside as I entered. Our business was soon done. He gave me the letter. At this instant there was a sound at the door. There were steps in the passage. Lucas quickly turned back the rug, thrust the document into some hiding-place there, and covered it over. What happened after that is like some fearful dream? I have a *vision* of a dark, *frantic* face, of a woman's voice, which screamed in French, 'My waiting is not in vain. At last, at last I have found you with her!' There was a savage struggle. I saw a knife in the woman's hand. I rushed from the horrible scene, and only next morning in the paper did I learn the dreadful result.

"My husband's *anguish* at the loss of his paper went to my heart. I could hardly prevent myself from there and then kneeling down at his feet and telling him what I had done. For two days I watched Lucas's place, but the door was never left open. Last night I made a last attempt. What I did and how I succeeded, you have already learned. I brought the paper back with me, and thought of destroying it, since I could see no way of returning it without confessing my guilt to my husband. Heavens, I hear his step upon the stair!"

The European Secretary burst excitedly into the room.

"Any news, Mr. Holmes, any news?" he cried.

"I have some hopes."

"Ah, thank heaven!" His face became *radiant*. "The Prime Minister is lunching with me. May he share your hopes? As to you, dear, I fear that this is a matter of politics. We will join you in a few minutes in the dining room."

The Prime Minister's manner was subdued, but I could see by the *gleam* of his eyes that he shared the excitement of his young colleague.

"The more I think of the matter," said Holmes, "the more convinced I am that the letter has never left this house. If it had it would certainly have been public by now."

"But why should anyone take it in order to keep it in his house?"

"I am not convinced that anyone did take it. Have you examined the box since Tuesday morning?"

"No. It was not necessary."

"You may *conceivably* have *overlooked* it. I have known such things to happen. I presume there are other papers there. Well, it may have got mixed with them."

"No, no, I had everything out."

"Surely it is easily, decided, Hope," said the Premier. "Let us have the dispatch box brought in. "

The Secretary rang the bell.

"Jacobs, bring down my dispatch box. This is a waste of time. Thank you, Jacobs, put it here. Here are the papers, you see. Letter from Lord Merrow, report from Sir Charles Hardy, letter from Madrid — Good heavens! What is this?"

The Premier snatched the blue envelope from his hand.

"Yes, it is it — and the letter is *intact*. Hope, I congratulate you. "

"Thank you! Thank you! What a weight from my heart. But this is *inconceivable* — impossible. Mr. Holmes, you are a wizard! How did you know it was there?"

"Because I knew it was nowhere else. "

"I cannot believe my eyes!" He ran wildly to the door. "Where is my wife? I must tell her that all is well. Hilda! Hilda!" we heard his voice on the stairs.

The Premier looked at Holmes with *twinkling* eyes.

"Come, sir," said he. "There is more in this than

meets the eye. How came the letter back in the box?"

Holmes turned away smiling from the keen *scrutiny* of those wonderful eyes.

"We also have our *diplomatic* secrets," said he and, picking up his hat, he turned to the door.

注释

resolution [ˌrezəˈljuːʃən] *n.* 决心

reluctance [riˈlʌktəns] *n.* 不愿

appropriate [əˈprəuprieit] *adj.* 适当的，合适的

episode [ˌepiˈsɔd] *n.* 一段情

culminate [ˈkʌlmineit] *v.* 达到顶点

consent [kənˈsent] *n.* 同意

decade [ˈdekeid] *n.* 十年

humble [ˈhʌmbl] *adj.* 粗陋的

honorable [ˈɔnərəbl] *adj.* 可敬的，光荣的

complication [kɔmpliˈkeiʃən] *n.* 复杂化，复杂因素

dispatch [disˈpætʃ] *n.* 急件

pledge [pledʒ] *n.* 保证，誓言

solemn [ˈsɔləm] *adj.* 庄严的

consequence [ˈkɔnsikwəns] *n.* 结果

wax [wæks] *n.* 蜡，蜡状物

continuation [kənˌtinjuˈeiʃən] *n.* 继续，延续

accustomed [əˈkʌstəmd] *adj.* 习惯的

resume [riˈzjuːm] *v.* 恢复

patriotism [ˈpætriətizəm, ˈpei-] *n.* 爱国精神

misfortune [misˈfɔːtʃən] *n.* 不幸，灾祸

provocative [prəˈvɔkətiv] *adj.* 刺激的，激怒的

uproar [ˈʌprɔ:] *n.* 喧嚣，骚动

superiority [sju(:)piˈɔriti] *n.* 优越

secure [siˈkjuə] *v.* 取得，赢得

breach [bri:tʃ] *n.* 破裂，裂口

tolerably [ˈtɔlərəb(ə)li] *adv.* 还算过得去地，还算不错地

immersed [iˈmə:st] *adj.* 沉入的，浸入的

sensational [senˈseiʃənəl] *adj.* 耸人听闻的

bid [bid] *n.* 出价，投标

personality [ˌpə:sənæliti] *n.* 个性，人格

curve [kə:v] *v.* 使弯曲

coincidence [kəuˈinsidəns] *n.* 巧合

distinguished [disˈtiŋgwiʃt] *adj.* 著名的，高贵的

feature [ˈfi:tʃə] *n.* 面目的一部分特征，容貌

overtake [ˈəuvəteik] *v.* 压倒，超过

occurrence [əˈkʌrəns] *n.* 事件

enlighten [inˈlaitn] *v.* 启发

resolve [riˈzɔlv] *v.* 消除，分解

haunted [ˈhɔ:ntid] *adj.* 受折磨的

startle [ˈstɑ:tl] *v.* 使震惊

Parisian [pəˈrizjən] *adj.* 巴黎人的，巴黎的

authority [ɔ:ˈθɔriti] *n.* 当局，官方

insane [inˈsein] *adj.* 患精神病的

insanity [inˈsæniti] *n.* 精神错乱，疯狂

permanent [ˈpə:mənənt] *adj.* 持久的

sensation [senˈseiʃən] *n.* 引起轰动的人或事

reestablishment [ˈri:isˈtæbliʃmənt] *n.* 重建，恢复

trivial [ˈtriviəl] *adj.* 微不足道的，琐细的

catastrophe [kəˈtæstrəfi] *n.* 大灾难

suspicion [səsˈpiʃən] *n.* 怀疑

stroll [strəul] *v.* 漫步

The Adventure of The Second Stain

portion [ˈpɔːʃən] *n.* 一部分

spill [spil] *n.* 溅出,溢出

stain [stein] *n.* 污点

vibrate [vaiˈbreit] *v.* 感情激动,振动

inward [ˈinwəd] *adj.* 内在的

dart [ˈdɑːt] *v.* 飞奔

bully [ˈbuli] *v.* 威吓,威逼

claw [klɔː] *v.* 抓

hinge [hindʒ] *v.* 靠铰链转动

cavity [ˈkæviti] *n.* 洞,空穴

plunge [plʌndʒ] *v.* 使插入

resigned [riˈzaind] *adj.* 听天由命的,能容忍的

confess [kənˈfes] *v.* 承认,坦白

shamefacedly [ʃeimˈfeistli] *adv.* 着愧地,着怯地

polished [ˈpɔliʃt] *adj.* 擦亮的,磨光的

repentant [riˈpentənt] *adj.* 悔改的

intently [inˈtentli] *adv.* 专心地

setback [ˈsetbæk] *n.* 坐折,退步

indiscreet [ˌindisˈkriːt] *adj.* 轻率的

management [ˈmænidʒmənt] *n.* 手段,操纵

residence [ˈrezidəns] *n.* 住处,居住

inquire [inˈkwaiə] *v.* 调查

indignation [ˌindigneiʃən] *n.* 愤慨,义愤

compromise [ˈkɔmprəmaiz] *v.* 危害,损害

alternative [ɔːlˈtəːnətiv] *n.* 可选择的事物

adjust [ədʒʌst] *v.* 调整,使合适

a stroke of luck 意外的好运

bosom [ˈbuzəm] *n.* 胸部

stuff [stʌf] *v.* 塞满,填满

impulsive [imˈpʌlsiv] *adj.* 冲动的

convey [kən'vei] *v.* 传达

vision ['viʒən] *n.* 景象

frantic ['fræntik] *adj.* 疯狂的

anguish ['æŋgwiʃ] *n.* 痛苦,苦恼

radiant ['reidjənt] *adj.* 容光焕发的

gleam [gli:m] *n.* 闪光,(喻)感情的闪现

conceivably [kən'si:vəbli] *adv.* 可能地,令人信服地

overlook [,əuvəluk] *v.* 没注意到

intact [in'tækt] *adj.* 原封未动的,完整无缺的

inconceivable [,inkən'si:vəbl] *adj.* 难以置信的,难以想象的

twinkling ['twiŋkliŋ] *adj.* 闪烁的,闪亮的

scrutiny ['skru:tini] *n.* 仔细研究,详细审查

diplomatic [,diplə'mætik] *adj.* 外交的

THE ADVENTURE OF CHARLES AUGUSTUS MILVERTON

It is years since the incidents of which I speak took place, and yet it is with *timidity* that I allude to them. For a long time, even with the utmost *discretion* it would have been impossible to make the facts public, but now the *principal* person concerned is beyond the reach of human law, and with due *suppression* the story may be told in such fashion as to injure no one. It records an absolutely unique experience in the career both of Mr. Sherlock Holmes and of myself.

We had been out for one of our evening walks, Holmes and I, and had returned about six o'clock on a cold, frosty winter's evening. As Holmes turned up the lamp the light fell upon a card on the table. He glanced at it, and then, with a cry of disgust, threw it on the floor. I picked it up and read:

"Charles Augustus Milverton, Appledore Towers, Hampstead. *Agent*."

"Who is he?" I asked.

"The worst man in London," Holmes answered, as he sat down and stretched his legs before the fire.

"Is anything on the back of the card?"

I turned it over.

"*Will call at* 6:30 — C. A. M. ," I read.

"*Hum*! He's about due. My disgust for this fellow is *exceeding*, and yet I can't get out of doing business with him — indeed, he is here at my invitation."

"But who is he?"

"He is the king of all the *blackmailers*... a *genius* in his way. His method is as follows: He *purchases* letters which compromise people of wealth and position. He receives these wares from thieves of all sorts, and pays them exceedingly well. Then he *threatens* the author of the letter with public *exposure* and demands great sums of money from them. A truly awful creature!"

I had seldom heard my friend speak with such *intensity* of feeling.

"But surely," said I, "the fellow must be within the grasp of the law?"

"It would seem so, but everyone fears to cross him."

"And why is he coming here?"

"Because a client has placed her case in my

hands. It is the Lady Eva Blackwell. She is to be married in a fortnight to the Earl of Dovercourt. Milverton has several *imprudent* letters, which were written to a young boy in the country. They would *suffice* to break off the match. Milverton will send the letters to the Earl unless a large sum of money is paid him. I have been *commissioned* to meet him, and — to make the best terms I can."

At that instant there was a knock at the door, and a small, stout man in an overcoat soon entered the room. Charles Augustus Milverton was a man of fifty, with a large, intellectual head, a round, plump, hairless face, and a *perpetual* frozen smile. As he advanced with a plump little hand extended, *murmuring* his regret for having missed us at his first visit, Holmes *disregarded* the outstretched hand and looked at him with a face of granite. Milverton's smile broadened, he shrugged his shoulders removed his overcoat, folded it with great *deliberation* over the back of a chair, and then took a seat.

"You are acting for Lady Eva," he said. "Has she empowered you to accept my terms?"

"What are your terms?"

"Seven thousand pounds."

"And the alternative?"

"My dear sir, it is painful for me to discuss it, but if the money is not paid on the 14th, there certainly will be no marriage on the 18th."

"I shall simply counsel my client to tell her future husband the whole story and to trust to his *generosity*."

"You evidently do not know the Earl," said Milverton, chuckling. "I can assure you that he would fail to appreciate her lively writing. However, if you think that it is in the best interests of your client that these letters should be placed in the hands of the Earl, then you would indeed be foolish to pay so large a sum of money to regain them."

He rose and seized his coat. Holmes was gray with anger.

"Wait a little," Holmes said. "You go too fast. We should certainly make every effort to avoid scandal in so delicate a matter."

"I was sure that you would see it in that light," he said, resettling into his chair.

"Lady Eva is not a wealthy woman. I assure you that even just two thousand pounds would be a *drain* upon her *resources*."

"I am aware of the lady's resources," said Milverton. "At the same time you must admit that it's likely she'll receive many a wedding gift."

"Still, it is impossible," said Holmes.

"How unfortunate!" cried Milverton, "To lose her husband for such a *beggarly* sum which she could easily get by turning her diamonds into *paste*. And you, a man of sense, going on about terms, when your client's future and honor are *at stake*. You surprise me, Mr. Holmes."

"Surely it is better for you to take the *substantial* sum which I offer than to ruin this woman's career, which can *profit* you in no way?"

"There you make a mistake, Mr. Holmes. It would make a good example to all of my other pending cases."

Holmes sprang from his chair.

"Get behind him, Watson! Don't let him out! Now, sir, let us see the contents of your pockets."

Milverton had glided as quick as a rat to the side of the room and stood with his back against the wall.

"Mr. Holmes," he said, turning the front of his coat and *exhibiting* the butt of a large revolver, which projected from the inside pocket. "You think me fool enough to bring the letters with me? Well, it seems our meeting is over, then, and it is a long drive to Hampstead. "

He stepped forward, took up his coat, laid his hand on his revolver, and turned to the door. Then, with a bow, a smile, and a twinkle, Milverton was out of the room.

Holmes sat for half-an-hour motionless by the fire. Then, with the gesture of a man who has taken his decision, he sprang to his feet and passed into his bedroom. A little later a young workman, with a goatee beard, lit his clay pipe at the lamp before *descending* into the street.

"I'll be back some time, Watson," said he, and vanished into the night.

For some days Holmes came and went at all hours in this *disguise*, without telling me what he was up to. At last, however, on a wild, stormy evening, he returned from his last expedition, and having removed his disguise he sat before the fire and laughed heartily in his silent inward fashion.

"You would not call me a marrying man, Watson?"

"No, indeed!"

"You'll be interested to hear that I'm engaged."

"My dear fellow! *Congrats—*"

"To Milverton's housemaid. It was a most necessary step. I am a plumber with a rising business, Escott, by name. I have walked out with her each evening, and through her I have gotten to know Milverton's house as I know the palm of my hand. Ah! What a splendid night it is!"

"You like this weather?"

"It suits my purpose. Watson, I mean to rob Milverton's house tonight."

I had a catching of the breath, and my skin went cold at the words, which were slowly uttered in a tone of *concentrated* resolution.

"For heaven's sake, Holmes, think what you are doing," I cried.

"My dear fellow, I have given it every consideration. I am justified so long as my object is to take no articles save those which are used for an *illegal* purpose. There is no other possible way of regaining these letters. Tomorrow is the last day of grace, and unless I can get the letters tonight, this villain will be as good as his word and will bring about her ruin. Besides, my self-respect and my *reputation* are in' need of repair since his visit. "

"Well, I don't like it, but I suppose it must be," said I.

"You know, Watson, I don't mind confessing to you that I have always had an idea that I would have made a highly *efficient* criminal. This is the chance of my lifetime in that direction. See here!"

He took a neat little leather case out of a drawer, and opening it he *exhibited* a number of shining instruments.

"This is a first-class thief's kit with all the necessary equipment. Have you a mask?"

"I can make a couple out of black silk. "

"Very good. It is now nine-thirty. At eleven we shall *depart*. Milverton is a heavy sleeper, and retires punctually at ten thirty. "

Holmes and I put on our dress clothes, so that we might appear to be coming from the theater. In Oxford Street we picked up a carriage and drove to an address in Hampstead. Here we paid off our cab, and walked the rest of the way.

"The documents are contained in a safe in the fellow's study, and the study is the room next to his bedroom. This is the house, this big one in its own grounds. We might put on our masks here, I think. You see. All the lights are out. "

With our black silk masks we stole up to the silent, gloomy house, and went around back to where a *greenhouse* stood, attached to the house.

The place was locked, but Holmes, taking a sharp blade, removed a circle of glass and turned the key from the inside. An instant afterwards he had closed the door behind us, and we had become criminals in the eyes of the law.

We passed through several rooms and down a rather long hall, until we reached a room with a fire still burning in the fireplace. The air was heavy with tobacco smoke. We were in Milverton's study, just next door to his bedroom.

In the corner, between a bookcase and the wall, there stood a tall, green safe, the *firelight* flashing back from the polished *brass knobs* upon its face. Holmes stole across and looked at it. Then he crept to the door of the bedroom, and stood with slanting head listening intently. No sound came from within. Meanwhile, it had struck me that it would be wise to secure our *retreat* through the outer door, so I examined it. To my amazement, it was neither locked nor *bolted.* I touched Holmes on the arm, and he turned his masked face in that direction. I saw him start, and he was evidently as surprised as I.

"I don't like it," he whispered, putting his lips to my very ear. "I can't quite make it out. Anyhow, we have no time to lose. Stand by the door. If you hear anyone come, bolt it on the inside, and we can get away as we came. If they come the other way, we can get through the door if our job is done, or hide behind these window curtains if it is not. Do you understand?"

I nodded, and stood by the door. With a glow of admiration I watched Holmes as he worked on the safe with concentrated energy, laying down one tool, picking up another, handling each with the strength and *delicacy* of the trained *mechanic.* Finally I heard a click, the broad green door swung open, and inside I had a *glimpse* of a number of paper packets. Holmes picked one out, but it was as hard to read by the flickering fire. Suddenly I saw Holmes *halt,* listen intently, and then in an instant he had swung the door of the safe closed, picked up his coat, stuffed his tools into the pockets, and darted behind the window curtain, motioning me to do the same.

It was only when I had joined him there that I heard what had alarmed his quicker senses. There was a noise of heavy footsteps rapidly approaching. They were in the passage outside the room. They paused at the door. The door opened. There was a sharp 'click' as the electric light was turned on. Then the footsteps came within a few yards of us. There was a creak from a chair, and the footsteps ceased. Then a key clicked in a lock, and I heard the rustle of papers.

Holmes and I carefully looked out from the curtains. Right in front of us, and almost within our reach, was the broad, rounded back of Milverton. It was evident that we had entirely *miscalculated* his movements, that he had never been to his bedroom, but that he had been sitting up in some smoking or billiard room in the farther wing of the house, the windows of which we had not seen. He was sitting at a desk in the middle of the room, leaning far back in a red leather chair. In his hand he held a long, legal document which he was reading in a lazy fashion, blowing rings of tobacco smoke from his lips as he did so. There was no promise of a speedy departure in his *composed* bearing and his comfortable attitude.

I then saw that the door of the safe was imperfectly closed, and that Milverton might at any moment observe it. In my own mind I had determined that if he were to notice, I would at once spring out, throw my great coat over his head, hold him, and leave the rest to Holmes.

But Milverton never looked up. He was interested in the papers in his hand.

Then a faint sound reached my ears from the balcony outside. Milverton dropped his papers and sat rigid in his chair. The sound was repeated, and then there came a gentle tap at the door. Milverton rose and opened it.

"Well," said he, rudely, "you are nearly half an hour late."

So this was the explanation of the unlocked door. There was the gentle rustle of a woman's dress. Soon, in front of him, in the full glare of the electric light, there stood a tall, slim, dark woman with a veil over her face. Her breath came quick and fast, and every inch of her figure was quivering with strong emotion.

"What are you *shivering* about? Pull yourself together. That's right. Now, let us get down to business." He took a notebook from the drawer of his desk. "You say that you have five letters which compromise the Countess d'Albert. You want to sell them. I want to buy them. So far so good. It only remains to fix a price. I should want to inspect the letters, of course. If they are really good *specimens* — Great heavens, is it you?"

The woman, without a word, had raised her veil. It was a dark, handsome, clear-cut face which *confronted* Milverton.

"It is I," she said, "the woman whose life you have ruined."

Milverton laughed, but fear *vibrated* in his voice. "You were so very *stubborn*," said he. "Why did you drive me to such *extremities*? I put the price well within your means. You would not pay."

"So you sent the letters to my husband, and he — the noblest gentleman that ever lived — he broke his gallant heart and died. I begged and prayed you for mercy, and you laughed in my face as you are trying to laugh now. Yes, you never thought to see me here again. Well, Charles Milverton, what have you to say?"

"Don't imagine that you can *bully* me," said he,

rising to his feet. "I have only to raise my voice and I could call my servants and have you taken to jail."

The woman stood with her hand buried in her bosom, her mouth spread in a deadly smile.

"You will ruin no more lives as you have ruined mine. I will free the world of a poisonous thing. Take that, you *hound* — and that! — and that! — and that!"

She had drawn a little *gleaming* revolver, and emptied barrel after barrel into Milverton's body, the muzzle within two feet of his shirt front. He shrank away and then fell forward upon the table, coughing *furiously* and clawing among the papers. Then he staggered to his feet, received another shot, and rolled upon the floor. The woman looked at him intently, and ground her heel into his face. She looked again, but there was no sound or movement. I heard a sharp rustle, the night air blew into the heated room, and the avenger was gone.

Hardly had the woman rushed from the room when Holmes, with swift, silent steps, was over at the other door. He turned the key in the lock. At the same instant we heard voices in the house and the sound of hurrying feet. He then slipped across to the safe, filled his two arms with *bundles* of letters, and poured them all into the fire. Again and again he did it, until the safe was empty. Someone turned the handle and beat upon the outside of the door. Holmes looked swiftly round, drew the key from the outer door, passed through after me, and locked it on the outside. "This way, Watson," said he, "we can *scale* the garden wall in this direction."

The whole front of the house was full of people in a state of alarm. One fellow saw us as we emerged from the balcony and followed hard at our heels. We came to a six-foot wall, which barred our path. Holmes sprang to the top and over. As I did the same I felt the hand of the man behind me grab at my ankle, but I kicked myself free and *scrambled* over. I fell upon my face among some bushes, but Holmes had me on my feet in an instant, and together we dashed away across the huge *expanse* of Hampstead Heath.

The next day, after breakfast, Lestrade, of Scotland Yard, paid us a visit.

"Good morning, Mr. Holmes," said he; "I thought that, perhaps, if you had nothing particular on hand, you might care to assist us in a most remarkable case, which occurred only last night at Hampstead. "

"Dear me!" said Holmes. "What was that?"

"A murder — a most *dramatic* and remarkable murder. We have had our eyes upon this Mr. Milverton for some time, and, between ourselves, he was a bit of a villain. Anyway, we know that the murderers were two men. They were nearly caught. One of them was stopped by the *gardener*, and only got away after a struggle. He was a middle-sized, strongly built man-square jaw, thick neck, moustache, a mask over his eyes. "

"That's rather vague," said Sherlock Holmes. "My, it might be a description of Watson!"

"It's true," said the inspector, with amusement. "It might be a description of Watson. "

"Well, I'm afraid I can't help you, Lestrade," said Holmes. "The fact is that I knew this fellow Milverton, that I considered him one of the most dangerous men in London, and my *sympathies* are with the criminals rather than with the victim. I will not handle this case. "

All that morning Holmes was in a most thoughtful mood, and seemed to be *striving* to *recall* something to his memory. We were in the middle of our lunch, when he suddenly sprang to his feet. "By Jove, Watson, I've got it!" he cried. "Come with me!"

He hurried at his top speed down Baker Street and along Oxford Street, until we had almost reached Regent Circus. Here, on the left hand, there stands a shop window filled with photographs of the *celebrities* and beauties of the day. Holmes's eyes fixed themselves upon one of them, and following his gaze I saw the picture of a lady in court dress. Then I caught my breath as I read the time-honored title of the great nobleman and statesman whose wife she had been. My eyes met those of Holmes, and he put his finger to his lips as we turned away from the window.

注释
___

timidity [tiˈmiditi] *n.* 胆怯

discretion [disˈkreʃən] *n.* 谨慎

principal [ˈprinsəp(ə)l, -sip-] *adj.* 主要的，首要的

suppression [səˈpreʃən] *n.* 抑制，镇压

agent [ˈeidʒənt] *n.* 代理人

hum [hʌm] *int.* 哼(表示不满、犹豫等)

exceeding [ikˈsiːdiŋ] *adj.* 非常的，极度的

blackmailer [ˈblækmeilə] *n.* 敲诈者，勒索者

genius ['dʒiːnjəs] *n.* 天才人物

purchase ['pɔːtʃəs] *v.* 购买

threaten [θretn] *v.* 威协

exposure [iks'pəuʒə] *n.* 揭露，曝光

intensity [in'tensiti] *n.* 强烈，剧烈

imprudent [im'pruːdənt] *adj.* 轻率的，鲁莽的

suffice [sə'fais] *v.* 足够，有能力

commission [kə'miʃən] *v.* 委托，委任

perpetual [pə'petjuəl] *adj.* 永久的

murmur ['məːmə] *v.* 低语

disregard [ˌdisri'gɑːd] *v.* 漠视

deliberation [diˌlibə'reiʃən] *n.* 从容，熟思

generosity [ˌdʒenə'rɔsiti] *n.* 慷慨，大方

drain [drein] *n.* 耗尽

resource [ri'sɔːs] *n.* 财力，资源

beggarly ['begəli] *adj.* 少得可怜的

paste [peist] *n.* （制人造宝石等用的）玻璃质混合物

at stake 濒临危险，得失攸关

substantial [səb'stænʃəl] *adj.* 真实的，实际上的

profit ['prɔfit] *vt.* 对…有利

exhibit [ˌeksi'bit] *v.* 显示，显出

descend [di'send] *v.* 下去

disguise [dis'gaiz] *n.* 伪装

congrats [kən'græts] *n.* 〈口〉祝贺，恭喜

concentrated ['kɔnsentreitid] *adj.* 强烈的，集中的

illegal [i'liːgəl] *adj.* 违法的

reputation [ˌrepjuː'teiʃən] *n.* 名誉，声望

efficient [i'fiʃənt] *adj.* 有效率的，能干的

exhibit [igzibit] *v.* 展出，陈列

kit [kit] *n.* 用具包，成套用具

The Adventure of Charles Augustus Milverton

depart [di'pɑːt] *v.* 出发

greenhouse ['griːnhaus] *n.* 温室,花房

firelight ['faiəlait] *n.* (炉)火光

brass [brɑːs] *adj.* 黄铜的

knob ['nɔb] *n.* 旋钮,按钮

creep [kriːp] *v.* 爬,蹑手蹑脚

retreat [ri'triːt] *n.* 撤退,退却

bolt [bəult] *v.* 上门闩

delicacy ['delikəsi] *n.* 微妙

mechanic [mi'kænik] *n.* 机械师,技工

glimpse [glimps] *n.* 一瞥,一看

halt [hɔːlt] *v.* 停止

miscalculate [ˌmis'kælkjuleit] *v.* 判断错误

composed [kəm'pəuzd] *adj.* 沉着的,镇静的

shiver ['ʃivə] *v.* 颤抖

specimen ['spesimən] *n.* 样品,样本

confront [kən'frʌnt] *v.* 使面临,面对

vibrate [vai'breit] *v.* 震动,激荡

stubborn ['stʌbən] *adj.* 顽固的,固执的

extremity [iks'tremiti] *n.* 困境,绝境

bully ['buli] *v.* 威吓

hound [haund] *n.* 卑鄙小人

gleaming [gliːmiŋ] *adj.* 发光的

furiously ['fjuəriəsli] *adv.* 猛烈地

bundle ['bʌndl] *n.* 捆,束

scale [skeil] *v.* 攀登

scramble ['skræmbl] *v.* 攀登

expanse [iks'pæns] *n.* 辽阔,广袤

dramatic [drə'mætik] *adj.* 戏剧性的

gardener ['gɑːdnə(r)] *n.* 园丁

sympathy [ˈsimpəθi] *n.* 同情,同情心

strive [straiv] *v.* 努力,力争

recall [riˈkɔːl] *v.* 回忆

celebrity [siˈlebriti] *n.* 名人

THE ADVENTURE OF THE EMPTY HOUSE

It was in the spring of the year 1894 that all London was interested, and the fashionable world *dismayed*, by the murder of the Honorable Ronald Adair under most unusual circumstances. The public has already learned those particulars of the crime, which came out in the police investigation, but a good deal was *suppressed* upon that occasion, since the case for the *prosecution* was so *overwhelmingly* strong that it was not necessary to bring forward all the facts. Only now, at the end of nearly ten years, am I allowed to supply those missing links which make up the whole of that remarkable chain. The crime was of interest in itself, but that interest was as nothing to me compared to the inconceivable follow-up, which afforded me the greatest shock and surprise of any event in my adventurous life.

It can be imagined that my close *intimacy* with Sherlock Holmes had interested me deeply in crime, and that after his disappearance I never failed to read with care the various problems which came before the public. There was none, however, which *appealed* to me like this tragedy of Ronald Adair. As I read the evidence at the trial, which led up to a verdict of will-ful murder against some person or persons unknown, I realized more clearly than I had ever done the loss which the *community* had *sustained* by the death of Sherlock Holmes. All day, as I drove upon my round, I turned over the case in my mind and found no explanation which appeared to me to be adequate. At the risk of telling a twice-told tale, I will go over the facts as they were known to the public at the con-clusion of the trial.

The Honorable Ronald Adair was the second son of the Earl of Maynooth, at that time *governor* of one of the Australian colonies. Adair's mother had re-turned from Australia to *undergo* an eye operation, and she, her son Ronald, and her daughter Hilda were living together at 427 Park Lane.

The youth moved in the best society, and had, so far as was known, no enemies and no particular vices. He was fond of card playing, but never for such stakes as would hurt him. He was a member of the Baldwin, the Cavendish, and the Bagatelle card clubs. It was shown that, after dinner on the day of his death, he had played a game at the latter club. He had also played there in the afternoon. The evidence of those who had played with him — Mr. Murray, Sir John Hardy, and Colonel Moran — showed that the game was *whist*. It came out in evidence that, in *partnership* with Colonel Moran, he had actually won as much as four hundred and twenty pounds in a sitting, some weeks before, from Godfrey Milner and Lord Balmoral.

On the evening of the crime, he returned from the club exactly at ten. His mother and sister were out spending the evening with a relation. At eleven thirty Lady Maynooth and her daughter returned home. Desiring to say goodnight, Lady Maynooth attempted to enter her son's room. The door was locked on the inside, and no answer could be got to their cries and knocking. Help was obtained, and the door forced. The unfortunate young man was found lying near the table. His head had been horribly injured by an *expanding* revolver bullet, but no weapon of any sort was to be found in the room. On the table lay money arranged in little piles of *varying* amounts. There were some figures also upon a sheet of paper, with the names of some club friends opposite to them, from which it was concluded that before his death he was endeavoring to make out his losses or winnings at cards.

Explanations for the locked door were hard to come by. There was no evidence to show that someone else had been in the room. Climbing up to the second storey window would have been impossible for there was no *drainpipe* leading up to it. Apparently, therefore, it was the young man himself who had fastened the door. But how did he come by his death? Suppose a man had fired through the window, he would indeed be a remarkable shot who could with a revolver *inflict* so deadly a wound. Again, Park Lane is a frequented area; there is a *cabstand* within a hundred yards of the house. No one had heard a shot.

Such were the circumstances of the Park Lane Mystery, which were further complicated by entire absence of motive, since, as I have said, young Adair was not known to have any enemies, and no attempt had been made to remove the money or valuables in the room.

In the evening I *strolled* across the Park, and found myself about six o'clock at the Oxford Street end of Park Lane. A group of loafers upon the *pavements*, all staring up at a particular window, directed me to the house which I had come to see. As I walked

toward the gathered crowd, I struck against an elderly, *deformed man*, who had been behind me, and I
knocked down several books which he was carrying. I
picked them up and handed them to him, apologizing,
but it was evident that these books were very precious
objects in the eyes of their owner. With a snarl of
contempt he turned upon his heel, and I saw his
curved back and white side burns disappear among the
throng.

My observations of 427 Park Lane did little to
clear up the problem in which I was interested. More
puzzled than ever, I *retraced* my steps to Kensington.
I had not been in my study five minutes when, to my
astonishment, I was paid a visit by the strange old
man whose books I had knocked from under his arm.

"Excuse me, Dr. Watson, I chanced to see you
go into this house. I thought to myself, I'll just step
in and tell him that if I was a bit rude in my manner
there was not any harm meant, and that I am much
obliged to him for picking up my books."

"You make too much of a trifle," said I. "May I
ask how you knew who I was?"

"Well, sir, if it isn't too great a *liberty*, I am a
neighbor of yours, for you'll find my little bookshop

at the corner of Church Street. Maybe you collect books yourself, sir. Although, from the untidy shelf behind you, I guess you don't?"

I moved my head to look at the *cabinet* behind me. When I turned again, Sherlock Holmes was standing smiling at me across my study table. I rose to my feet, stared at him for some seconds in utter amazement, and then it appears that I must have fainted for the first and the last time in my life. When I awoke, Holmes was standing over me.

"My dear Watson," said the well-remembered voice, "I owe you a thousand apologies. I had no idea that you would be so affected."

I *gripped* him by the arms.

"Is it really you, Holmes? Can it indeed be that you are alive? Is it possible that you succeeded in climbing out of that awful *chasm*?"

"I had no serious difficulty in getting out of it, for the very simple reason that I never was in it."

"You never were in it?"

"No, Watson. I'll admit I had little doubt that I had come to the end of my career when I perceived the sinister figure of the late Professor Moriarty standing upon the narrow pathway which led to safety. He drew no weapon, but rushed at me. He knew that his own game was up, and was only anxious to *revenge* himself upon me. We fought upon the *brink* of the waterfall. Thanks to my knowledge of the Japanese system of wrestling, I slipped through his grip, and he with a horrible scream, went over the edge. "

I listened with amazement to this explanation, which Holmes delivered between the *puffs* of his cigarette.

"But the tracks!" I cried. "I saw, with my own eyes, that two went down the path and none returned. "

"I knew that Moriarty was not the only man who had sworn my death. There were at least three others whose desire for vengeance upon me would only be increased by the death of their leader. However, if all the world was convinced that I was dead, I figured these men would soon lay themselves open, and sooner or later I could destroy them. So, instead of *faking* tracks in the wrong direction, I determined to climb up the cliff... an exceedingly dangerous task. More than once, as my foot slipped against the wet rock, I thought that I was gone. But I struggled upward, and at last I reached a ledge several feet deep, where I could lie unseen. There I was stretched, when you, my dear Watson, and all your followers were investigating in the most *sympathetic* and *inefficient* manner the circumstances of my death.

"At last, when you had all formed your *inevitable* and totally *erroneous* conclusions, you departed for the hotel. Looking up, however, I saw a man's head against the darkening sky, and a huge stone struck the very ledge upon which I was stretched, within a foot of my head. Of course, the meaning of this was obvious. Moriarty had not been alone. A confederate had kept guard while the Professor had attacked me. Now he was endeavoring to succeed where his comrade had failed.

"I did not take long to think about it, Watson. I scrambled down onto the path. I don't think I could have done it in cold blood. It was a hundred times more difficult than getting up. But I had no time to think of the danger, for another stone sang past me as I hung by my hands from the edge of the ledge. Halfway down I slipped, but, by the blessing of God, I landed, torn and bleeding, upon the path. I took to my heels, did ten miles over the mountains in the darkness, and a week later I found myself in Florence, with the certainty that no one in the world knew what had become of me.

"I *contacted* only one person — my brother Mycroft. I owe you many apologies, my dear Watson, but it was extremely important that it should be thought I was dead, and it is quite certain that you would not have written so *convincing* an account of my unhappy end had you not yourself thought that it was true. As to Mycroft, I had to confide in him in order to obtain the money which I needed. The course of events in London did not run so well as I had hoped, for the trial of the Moriarty gang left two of its most dangerous members at liberty. I traveled for two years in Tibet, therefore, and amused myself by visiting Lhassa. You may have read of the remarkable explorations of a Norwegian named Sigerson, but I am sure that it never occurred to you that you were receiving news of your friend. I then passed through Persia, and looked in at Mecca.

"Having traveled to my satisfaction and learning that only one of my enemies was now left in London, I was about to return when my movements were *hastened* by the news of this very remarkable Park Lane Mystery, which not only appealed to me by its own *merits*, but which seemed to offer some most peculiar personal opportunities. I came over at once to London, called in my own person at Baker Street, threw Mrs. Hudson into violent *hysterics*, and found that Mycroft had preserved my rooms and my papers exactly as they had always been. So it was, my dear Watson, that at two o'clock today I found myself in my old armchair in my own old room, and only wishing that I could have seen my old friend Watson in the other chair which he has so often adorned.

"Now, I have a piece of work for us both tonight which, if we can bring it to a successful conclusion, will explain things to an even greater extent. Now let us be off at once."

It was indeed like old times when I found myself seated beside him in a carriage, my revolver in my pocket, and the *thrill* of adventure in my heart. Holmes was cold and *stern* and silent. I knew not what wild beast we were about to hunt down in the dark jungle of criminal London, but I was well assured, from the bearing of this master huntsman, that the adventure was a most grave one.

I had imagined that we were bound for Baker Street, but Holmes stopped the cab at the corner of

Cavendish Square. I observed that as he stepped out he gave a most searching glance to right and left, and then he *submerged* himself into a network of narrow alleyways, the very existence of which I had never known. We turned swiftly down a narrow passage, passed through a wooden gate into a deserted yard, and then opened with a key the back door of a house. We entered together, and he closed it behind us.

The place was *pitch dark*, but it was evident to me that it was an empty house. Holmes's cold, thin fingers closed round my *wrist* and led me forward down a long hall. Holmes then turned suddenly to the right and we found ourselves in a large, square, empty room. It was so dark, we could only just *discern* each other's figures within.

"Do you know where we are?" Holmes whispered.

"Surely that is Baker Street" I answered, staring through the *dim* window.

"Exactly. We are just opposite my home."

"But why are we here?"

"Might I trouble you, my dear Watson, to draw a little nearer to the window, and to look up at our old rooms? We will see if my three years of absence have entirely taken away my power to surprise you. "

I crept forward and looked across at the familiar window. As my eyes fell upon it, I gave a gasp and a cry of amazement. The blind was down, and a strong light was burning in the room. The shadow of a man who was seated in a chair within was thrown in hard, black outline upon the *luminous* screen of the window. It was a perfect-*reproduction* of Holmes. So amazed was I that I threw out my hand to make sure that the man himself was standing beside me. He was quivering with silent laughter.

"Good heavens!" I cried. "It is *marvelous.* "

"It really is rather like me, is it not? The credit must go to Monsieur Oscar Meunier, who spent some days in making my bust from wax. The rest I arranged myself during my visit to Baker Street this afternoon. "

"But why?"

"Because, my dear Watson, I know my room is being watched by my enemies. And I do not wish it to be known that I have been out upon the town. This morning, they saw me return home for the first time in years. "

"How do you know?"

"Because I recognized their watchman when I glanced out of my window. He I worry little about. But I cared a great deal for the much more *formidable* person who was behind him, the bosom friend of Moriarty, the man who dropped the rocks over the cliff. That is the man who is after me tonight Watson, and that is the man who is quite *unaware* that we are after him."

My friend's plans were gradually revealing themselves. From this convenient retreat, the watchers were being watched and the trackers tracked. In silence we stood together in the darkness and watched the hurrying figures who passed and repassed in front of us. I especially noticed two men who appeared to be sheltering themselves from the wind in the doorway of a house some distance up the street. I tried to draw my companion's attention to them; but he showed little interest.

Ah! Holmes drew in his breath excitedly. An instant later he pulled me back into the blackest corner of the room, and I felt his warning hand upon my lips. The fingers which clutched me were quivering. Never had I known my friend more moved, and yet the dark street still stretched lonely and motionless before us.

But suddenly I was aware of that which his *keener* senses had already distinguished. A low, stealthy sound came to my ears, not from the direction of Baker Street, but from the back of the very house in which we lay *concealed. Peering* through the *gloom*, I saw the vague outline of a man, a shade blacker than the blackness of the open door. He stood for an instant, and then he crept forward, crouching, *menacing*, into the room. He was within three yards of us, this sinister figure; and I had *braced* myself to meet his spring, before I realized that he had no idea of our presence. He passed close beside us, stole over to the window, and very softly and noiselessly raised it for half a foot. As he sank to the level of this opening, the light of the street, no longer *dimmed* by the dusty glass, fell full upon his face. The man seemed to be beside himself with excitement.

In his hand he carried what appeared to be a stick, but as he laid it down upon the floor it made a *metallic* sound. For the next several minutes he busied himself in piecing together several objects he had hidden under his coat. Eventually, he finished and straightened himself, and I saw that what he held in

his hand was a sort of gun, with a curiously missha-
pen butt.

Crouching down, he rested the end of the barrel
upon the ledge of the open window, and I saw his eye
gleam as it peered along the sights. I heard a little
sigh of satisfaction as he eased the butt into his shoulder; and saw that amazing target, the black man on
the yellow ground, standing clear at the end of his
foresight. For an instant he was rigid and motionless.
Then his finger tightened on the *trigger*. There was a
strange silvery ringing of broken glass. At that instant Holmes sprang like a tiger onto the gunman's
back, and *hurled* him flat upon his face. He was up
again in a moment, and seized Holmes by the throat,
but I struck him on the head with the butt of my revolver, and he dropped again upon the floor. I fell
upon him, and as I held him my comrade blew a whistle. There was the clatter of running feet upon the
pavement, and two policemen in uniform, with one
plain-clothes detective, rushed through the front entrance and into the room.

"Thank you, Lestrade?" said Holmes.

"Yes, Mr. Holmes. I took the job myself. It's
good to see you back in London, sir."

We had all risen to our feet, our prisoner breathing hard, with two officers on either side of him. I was able at last to have a good look at him. It was a *tremendously* powerful and yet sinister face which was turned towards us. With the brow of a *philosopher* above and the jaw of a sensualist below, the man must have started with great capacities for good or for evil. He looked at no one but Holmes, staring with an expression in which hatred and amazement were equally blended.

"Clever beast!" he kept on muttering.

"Ah, Colonel!" said Holmes. "'Journeys end in lovers' meetings' as the old play says. I don't think I have had the pleasure of seeing you since you favored me with those attentions as I lay on the ledge above the waterfall."

The *colonel* only stared in silent anger.

"I have not introduced you yet," said Holmes. "This, gentlemen, is Colonel Sebastian Moran, once of Her *Majesty's* Indian Army, and the best heavy-game shot that our Eastern Empire has ever produced."

Colonel Moran sprang forward with a snarl of *rage*, but the officers dragged him back. The *fury* upon his face was terrible to look at.

"I confess that you had one small surprise for me," said Holmes. "I did not anticipate that you would yourself make use of this empty house and this convenient front window. I had imagined you as operating from the street, where my friend Lestrade and his merry men were awaiting you. With that exception, all has gone as I expected."

Holmes then picked up the powerful air gun from the floor and examined its *mechanism*.

"An admirable and unique weapon," said he, "noiseless and of *tremendous* power: I knew Von Herder, the blind German mechanic, who constructed it to the order of the late Professor Moriarty. I *commend* it very specially to your attention, Lestrade, and also the bullets which fit it."

"You can trust us to look after that, Mr. Holmes," said Lestrade, as the whole party moved towards the door. "Anything further to say?"

"Only to ask what charge you intend to prefer?"

"What charge, sir? Why, of course, the attempted murder of Mr. Sherlock Holmes."

"Not so, Lestrade. I do not propose to appear in the matter at all. To you, and to you only, belongs the credit of the remarkable arrest which you have effected. Congratulations, Lestrade, you have got him. "

"Got him! Got whom, Mr. Holmes?"

"The man who shot the Honorable Ronald Adair with an expanding bullet from an air-gun through the open window of the second-floor front of 427 Park Lane, upon the thirtieth of last month. And now, Watson, if you can *endure* the *draught* from a broken window, I think that half an hour in my study over a cigar may afford you some profitable amusement. "

Our old *chambers* had been left unchanged through the *supervision* of Mycroft Holmes and the immediate care of Mrs. Hudson. The strange wax figure, which had played so important a part in the evening's adventures, sat upon a *pedestal* in the middle of the room.

"Excellent!" said Holmes, approaching the pedestal. "Plumb in the middle of the back of the head and smack through the brain. He was the best shot in India, and I expect that there are few better in London. Have you heard the name?"

"No, I have not. "

"Well, well, such is fame! Moran, Sebastian, Colonel. Unemployed. Formerly 1st Bangalore Pioneers. Served in Jowaki Campaign, Afghan Campaign, and numerous others. Member of The Anglo-Indian, the Tankerville, the Bagatelle card clubs. "

"Astonishing," said I "The man's career is that of an honorable soldier. "

"It is true," Holmes answered. "And yet, whatever the cause, Colonel Moran began to go wrong. He retired, came to London, and acquired an evil name. It was at this time that he was sought out by Professor Moriarty, to whom for a time he was chief of staff. Moriarty supplied him *liberally* with money, and used him only in one or two very high-class jobs, which no ordinary criminal could have *undertaken.*

"Of course, after the death of Moriarty, had I stayed in London, night and day, Moran's shadow would have been over me, and sooner or later his chance must have come. What could I do? While away, I watched the criminal news, knowing that sooner or later I should get him. Then came the death of this Ronald Adair. My chance had come at last. Knowing what I did, was it not certain that Colonel Moran had done it? He had played cards with the lad; he had followed him home from the club; he had shot him through the open window. There was not a doubt of it. The bullets alone are enough to hang him. I came over at once. I was seen by their watchman, who would, I knew, direct the colonel's attention to my presence. He could not fail to connect my sudden return with his crime, and to be terribly alarmed. I was sure that he would make an attempt to get me out of the way at once, and would bring round his murderous weapon for that purpose. Now, my dear Watson, does anything remain for me to explain?"

"Yes," said I. "You have not made it clear what was Colonel Moran's motive in murdering the Honorable Ronald Adair?"

"Ah! My dear Watson, it came out in evidence that Colonel Moran and young Adair had, between them, won a considerable amount of money. Now, undoubtedly Moran had cheated. I believe that on the day of the murder Adair had discovered that Moran was cheating. Very likely he had spoken to him privately, and had threatened to expose him unless he *voluntarily* resigned his *membership* of the club, and promised not to play cards again. The *exclusion* from his clubs would mean ruin to Moran, who lived by his ill-gotten card gains. He, therefore, murdered Adair, who at the time was endeavoring to work out how much money he should himself return, since he could not profit by his partner's foul play. He locked the door lest the ladies should surprise him and insist upon knowing what he was doing with these names and coins. Will it pass?"

"I have no doubt that you have hit upon the truth."

"It will be *verified* or disproved at the trial. Meanwhile, come what may, Colonel Moran will trouble us no more, and once again Mr. Sherlock Holmes is free to devote his life to examining those interesting little problems which the complex life of London so *plentifully* presents."

注释

---

dismay [dis'mei] *v.* 使惊慌，使沮丧

suppress [sə'pres] *v.* 隐瞒，不让发表

prosecution [,prɔsi'kju:ʃən] *n.* 起诉

overwhelmingly [,əuvə'welmiŋli] *adv.* 压倒性地，不可抵抗地

intimacy ['intiməsi] *n.* 亲密

appeal [ə'pi:l] *v.* 引起兴趣

community [kə'mju:niti] *n.* 社会

sustain [səs'tein] *v.* 蒙受，遭受

governor ['gʌvənə] *n.* 统治者，总督

undergo [,ʌndə'gəu] *v.* 经历，遭受

whist [(h)wist] *n.* 扑克牌游戏的一种（惠斯特）

partnership ['pɑːtnəʃip] *n.* 合伙关系

expanding [iks'pændiŋ] *adj.* 展开的,扩大的

varying ['vɛəriŋ] *adj.* 各种各样的

drainpipe ['dreinpaip] *n.* 排水管

inflict [in'flikt] *v.* 造成

cabstand ['kæbstænd] *n.* 出租车停车场

stroll ['strəul] *v.* 漫步,闲逛

pavement ['peivmənt] *n.* 人行道,公路

deformed [di'fɔːmd] *adj.* 丑陋的,残废的

contempt [kən'tempt] *n.* 请示,不尊重

retrace [ri'treis] *v.* 折回

liberty ['libəti] *n.* 冒失,冒昧

cabinet ['kæbinit] *n.* 橱柜

grip [ɡrip] *v.* 抓住

chasm ['kæzəm] *n.* 峡谷,深渊

revenge [ri'vendʒ] *v.* 复仇

brink [briŋk] *n.* (峭岸、崖的)边缘

puff [pʌf] *n.* 喷出,吹气

fake ['feik] *v.* 伪造

sympathetic ['simpəθetik] *adj.* 有同情心的

inefficient [ini'fiʃənt] *adj.* 无能的,不能胜任的

inevitable [in'evitəbl] *adj.* 不可避免的,必然的

erroneous [i'rəunjəs] *adj.* 错误的

contact ['kɔntækt] *v.* 联系

convincing [kən'vinsiŋ] *adj.* 令人信服的

hasten ['heisn] *v.* 促进,加速

merit [merit] *n.* 真相,是非曲直

hysterics [hi'steriks] *n.* 歇斯底里的发作,发疯

thrill [θril] *n.* 激动,兴奋

stern [stəːn] *adj.* 严格的,严厉的

The Adventure of The Empty House

submerge [səbˈmɚːdʒ] *v.* 掩没，淹没

pitch dark 非常黑

wrist [rist] *n.* 手腕，腕关节

discern [diˈsəːn] *v.* 辨别

dim [dim] *adj.* 暗淡的，模糊的

luminous [ˈljuːminəs] *adj.* 发光的，明亮的

reproduction [ˌriːprədʌkʃən] *n.* 重现，复制品

marvelous [ˈmɑːviləs] *adj.* 非凡的，不可思议的

formidable [ˈfɔːmidəbl] *adj.* 难对付的，可怕的

unaware [ˈʌnəwɛə] *adj.* 不知道的，难察觉的

keen [kiːn] *adj.* 敏锐的

conceal [kənˈsiːl] *v.* 隐藏，隐蔽

peer [piə] *v.* 凝视，窥视

gloom [gluːm] *n.* 阴暗

menace [ˈmenəs] *n.* 威胁、恐吓

brace [breis] *v.* 拉牢的

dim [dim] *v.* 使暗淡

metallic [miˈtælik] *adj.* 金属撞击声的

trigger [ˈtrigə] *n.* 扳机

hurl [həːl] *v.* 猛冲

tremendously [triˈmendəsli] *adv.* 非常地，可怕地

philosopher [fiˈlɔsəfə] *n.* 哲学家

colonel [ˈkəːnl] *n.* 陆军上校，团长

Majesty [ˈmædʒisti] *n.* (前面与 His, Her, Your 连用)陛下

rage [reidʒ] *n.* 愤怒，狂暴

fury [ˈfjuəri] *n.* 狂怒

mechanism [ˈmekənizəm] *n.* 机构，机械装置

tremendous [triˈmendəs] *adj.* 极大的，巨大的

commend [kəˈmend] *v.* 委托

endure [inˈdjuə] *v.* 忍受

draught [drɑːft] *n.* 气流

chamber ['tʃeimbə] *n.* 室,房间

supervision [ˌsjuːpəˈviʒən] *n.* 监督,管理

pedestal ['pedistl] *n.* 底座,基架

liberally ['libərəli] *adv.* 大方地

undertake [ˌʌndəˈteik] *v.* 承担,担任

voluntarily ['vɔləntərili] *adv.* 自动地,自愿地

membership ['membəʃip] *n.* 成员资格

exclusion [iksˈkluːʒən] *n.* 排除

verify ['verifai] *v.* 查证,核实

plentifully ['plentifuli] *adv.* 丰富地,大量地

THE ADVENTURE OF THE ENGINEER'S THUMB

Of all the problems which have been submitted to my friend, Mr. Sherlock Holmes, for solution during the years of our intimacy, there were only two which I was the means of introducing to his notice: that of Mr. Hatherley's thumb, and that of Colonel Warburton's madness. Of these the latter may have afforded a finer field for an *acute* and *original* observer, but the other was so strange in its origin and so dramatic in its details that it may be the more worthy of being placed upon record, even if it gave my friend fewer openings for those *deductive* methods of reasoning by which he achieved such remarkable results.

It was in the summer of '89, not long after my marriage, that the events occurred which I am now about to summarize. I had returned to civil practice and had finally abandoned Holmes in his Baker Street rooms, although I continually visited him. My practice had steadily increased, and as I happened to live at no very great distance from Paddington Station, I got a few patients from among the officials.

One morning, at a little before seven o'clock, I

was awakened by the maid tapping at the door to announce that two men had come from Paddington and were waiting in the *consulting* room. I dressed hurriedly and hastened downstairs. As I descended, the guard came out of the room and closed the door tightly behind him.

"I've got him here," he whispered, *jerking* his thumb over his shoulder; "It's a new patient. I thought I'd bring him round myself. There he is, all safe and sound. I must go now, Doctor." And off he went without even giving me time to thank him.

I entered my consulting room and found a gentleman seated by the table. Round one of his hands he had a handkerchief *wrapped*, which was covered with bloodstains. He was young, not more than twenty-five, I should say, with a strong, masculine face; but he was exceedingly pale and gave me the impression of a man who was suffering from some strong *agitation*, which it took all his strength of mind to control.

"I am sorry to wake you up so early, Doctor," said he, "but I have had a very serious accident during the night. I came in by train this morning, and on *inquiring* at Paddington as to where I might find a doctor, a worthy fellow very kindly escorted me here.

There's my name card on the table."

I took it up and glanced at it.

"Mr. Victor Hatherley, engineer, 16A, Victoria Street (3rd. floor)."

"I regret that I have kept you waiting," said I, sitting down in my library chair. "You are fresh from a night journey, I understand, which is in itself a *monotonous* occupation."

"Oh, my night could not be called monotonous," said he, and began to laugh *hysterically* for quite some time. Eventually he regained his composure, but seemed very weak.

"I have been making a fool of myself," he gasped.

"Not at all. Drink this." I dashed some brandy into the water, and the color began to come back to his bloodless cheeks.

"That's better!" said he. "And now, Doctor, perhaps you would kindly attend to my thumb, or rather to the place where my thumb used to be."

He unwound the handkerchief and held out his hand. It gave even my *hardened* nerves a shudder to look at it, for his thumb had been hacked or torn right out from the roots.

"Good heavens!" I cried, "This is a terrible injury. It must have bled considerably."

"Yes, it did. I fainted when it was done, and I think that I must have been senseless for a long time."

"This has been done," said I, examining the wound, "by a very heavy and sharp instrument."

"A thing like a butcher's knife," said he.

"An accident, I presume?"

"Not at all. More like a murderous attack."

"What! You horrify me!"

"I shall have to tell my tale to the police; but, between ourselves, if it were not for the convincing evidence of this wound of mine, I should be surprised if they believed my statement; for it is a very extraordinary one, and I have not much in the way of proof with which to back it up."

"Well, if it is anything in the nature of a problem which you desire to see solved, I should strongly recommend you to come to my friend, Mr. Sherlock Holmes, before you go to the official police."

"Yes! I know of him! Would you give me an introduction to him?"

"I'll do better. I'll take you round to him myself.

Just after I finish cleaning and dressing this hand of yours, we'll call a cab and go together. "

Twenty minutes later I was inside a carriage, driving with my new acquaintance to Baker Street.

Sherlock Holmes received us in his quietly polite fashion, ordered breakfast, and joined us in a hearty meal. When it was concluded he asked Mr. Hatherley to tell his story.

"Well, I'll begin by telling you that I am an engineer, with a number of years experience, *despite* my young age. Two years ago, after coming into a fair sum of money through my poor father's death, I determined to start in business for myself and took *professional* chambers in Victoria Street. It has been hard. In these two years, I have had three *consultations* and one small job. Every day, from nine in the morning until four in the afternoon, I waited in my little den, until at last my heart began to sink, and I came to believe that I should never have any practice at all.

"Yesterday, however, I was visited by a man, Colonel Lysander Stark. He was exceedingly thin, and his whole face sharpened away into nose and chin, and the skin of his cheeks was drawn quite tense over his *outstanding* bones.

"'Mr. Hatherley?' said he, with something of a German accent. "You have been recommended to me as being a man who is not only *proficient* in his profession but is also *discreet* and capable of *preserving* a secret.' I bowed, feeling as flattered as any young man would at such an address. 'I also hear that you are an *orphan*, *residing* alone in London,' he added.

"'That is quite correct,' I answered.

"'Good. I have a professional commission for you, but absolute secrecy is quite essential — thus we want someone with no family ties. Can you promise to keep what I say a secret?'"

"'Yes, I can,' I said.

"'Very good.' He suddenly sprang up, drew up his chair very close to mine and began to stare at me with a questioning and thoughtful look.

"A feeling of fear had begun to rise within me at the strange behavior of this fleshless man. Even my dread of losing a client could not *restrain* me from showing my impatience.

"'I beg that you will state your business, sir,' said I.

"'How would fifty *guineas* for a night's work

suit you?' he asked.

"'Most admirably,' I said.

"'I simply want your opinion about a water-pressured stamping machine which has got *out of gear*. If you show us what is wrong we shall soon set it right ourselves. We shall want you to come tonight by the last train. '

"'Where to?'

"'To Eyford, in Berkshire. It is a little place near the borders of Oxfordshire. I shall come down in a carriage to meet you, for our place is quite out in the country. It is a good seven miles from the station. '

"'That is very *awkward*. Could I not come at some more convenient hour?' I asked.

"'We have judged it best that you should come late. We feel the pay more than *compensates* the inconvenience. '

"I thought of the fifty guineas, and of how very useful they would be to me.

"'I shall be very happy to *accommodate* myself to your wishes, then,' I said. 'I should like, however, to understand a little more clearly what it is that you wish me to do. '

"'Quite so. You are probably aware that fuller's-earth is a valuable product, and that it is only found in one or two places in England?'

"'I have heard so.'I said

"'Some little time ago I bought a small place within ten miles of Reading. I was fortunate enough to discover that there was a *deposit* of fuller's earth in one of my fields. On examining it, however, I found that this deposit was a *comparatively* small one, and that it formed a link between two very much larger ones upon the right and left — both of them, however, in the grounds of my neighbors. Naturally, it was to my interest to buy their land before they discovered its true value, but unfortunately I had no capital by which I could do this. Thus, my friends and I have gone into business together and purchased a large press. The machine, as I've said, has got out of order, and we wish your advice upon the subject.'

"'I quite follow you,' said I. 'The only point which I could not quite understand was what use you could make of a press in digging fuller's earth?'

"'Ah!' said he carelessly, 'we have our own process. We compress the earth into bricks, so as to remove them without revealing what they are. But that is a mere detail. 'He rose as he spoke. ' I shall expect you, then, at Eyford at 11:15. '

"He then hurried from the room.

"Well, as I thought about things, I was glad, on the one hand, for the fee was at least tenfold what I should have asked had I set a price upon my own services. On the other hand, the face and manner of my *patron* had made an unpleasant impression upon me; yet, I threw all fears to the winds, ate a hearty supper, drove to Paddington, and started off.

"I was the only passenger who got out at Eyford. As I passed out through the gate, I found my acquaintance of the morning waiting in the shadow upon the other side. Without a word he grasped my arm and hurried me into a carriage, the door of which was standing open. He drew up the windows on either side, tapped on the door, and away we went as fast as the horse could go. "

"One horse?" interrupted Holmes.

"Yes, only one. "

"Tired-looking or fresh?"

"Oh, fresh and shiny. "

"Thank you. Please, continue your most interesting statement. "

"Away we went then, and we drove for at least an hour. Colonel Lysander Stark had said that it was only seven miles, but I should think, from the rate that we seemed to go, and from the time that we took, that it must have been nearer twelve. I tried to look out of the windows to see something of where we were, but they were made of frosted glass, and I could make out nothing save the occasional bright *blur* of a passing light. At last, however, the *bumping* of the road was exchanged for the crisp smoothness of a gravel drive, and the carriage came to a stand. We stepped, as it were, right out of the carriage and into the hall of a house, so that I failed to catch the most *fleeting* glance of the building's *exterior*. The instant that I had crossed the *threshold*, the door *slammed* heavily behind us, and I heard *faintly* the rattle of the wheels as the carriage drove away.

"A woman appeared with a lamp in her hand, which she held above her head, pushing her face forward and peering at us. She spoke a few words in German in a tone as though asking a question, and when my companion answered with a single word she gave such a start that the lamp nearly fell from her hand. Colonel Stark went up to her, whispered something in her ear, and then, pushing her back into the room from where she had come, he walked towards me again with the lamp in his hand.

"'Perhaps you will have the kindness to wait in this room for a few minutes,' said he, throwing open another door. It was a quiet, little, plainly furnished room.

"'I shall not keep you waiting an instant,' said the colonel, and he vanished into the darkness.

"A vague feeling of uneasiness began to steal over me. Who were these German people, and what were they doing living in this strange, out-of-the-way place? And where was the place? I had no idea.

"Suddenly, the door of my room swung slowly open. The woman was standing in the door. I could see at a glance that she was sick with fear, and the sight sent a *chill* to my own heart. She held up one shaking finger to warn me to be silent, and she shot a few whispered words of broken English at me, her eyes glancing back, like those of a frightened horse, into the gloom behind her.

"'You should go. It is not worth your while to wait,' she said. 'You can pass through the door; no one *hinders*.' And then, seeing that I smiled and

shook my head, she suddenly threw aside her con-
straint and made a step forward. 'For the love of
Heaven!' she whispered, 'get away from here before
it is too late!'

"But I am somewhat stubborn by nature, and the
more ready to engage in an affair when there is some
obstacle in the way. I thought of my fifty-guinea fee,
of my *wearisome* journey, and of the unpleasant night
which seemed to be before me. Was it all to go for
nothing? This woman might, for all I knew, be crazy. With a stout bearing, therefore, though her manner had shaken me more than I cared to confess, I
still shook my head and declared my intention of remaining where I was.

"The sound of several footsteps was heard upon
the stairs. She listened for an instant, threw up her
hands with a *despairing* gesture, and vanished as
suddenly and as noiselessly as she had come. The
newcomers were Colonel Lysander Stark and a short
thick man with a beard, who was introduced to me as
Mr. Ferguson.

"'Mr. Ferguson and I will take you upstairs to
see the machine.'

"'What, you dig fuller's earth in the house?' I

asked.

"'No, no. This is only where we compress it. But never mind that. All we wish you to do is to examine the machine and to let us know what is wrong with it.'

"We went upstairs together, the colonel first with the lamp, the fat manager and I behind him. I tried to put on as unconcerned an air as possible, but I had not forgotten the warnings of the lady, even though I disregarded them, and I kept a keen eye upon my two companions.

"Colonel Lysander Stark stopped at last before a low door, which he unlocked. Within was a small, square room, in which the three of us could hardly get at one time. Ferguson remained outside, and the colonel ushered me in.

"'We are now,' said he, 'actually within the press, and it would be a particularly unpleasant thing for us if anyone were to turn it on. The ceiling of this small *chamber* is really the end of the descending *piston*, and it comes down with the force of many tons upon this metal floor. The machine goes readily enough, but there is some *stiffness* in the working of it, and it has lost a little of its force. Perhaps you will have the goodness to look it over and to show us how we can set it right. '

"I took the lamp from him, and I examined the machine very thoroughly. It was indeed a *gigantic* one, and capable of exercising enormous pressure. When I passed outside, however, and pressed down the *levers* which controlled it, I knew at once by the sound that there was a slight leakage, which was clearly the cause of the loss of power, and I pointed it out to my companions, who followed my remarks very carefully and asked several practical questions as to how they should proceed to set it right. When I had finished, I *reentered* the room to have a look. It was clear that the story of the fuller's earth was false; for it would be absurd to suppose that so powerful an engine could be designed for so *inadequate* a purpose. I had *stooped* and was examining some metal deposits on the floor, when I heard a *muttered* exclamation in German and saw the face of the colonel looking down at me.

"'What are you doing there?' he asked.

"'I was admiring your fuller's earth,' said I; 'I think that I should be better able to advise you as to your machine if I knew what the exact purpose was for which it was used. '

"'Very well,' said he, 'you shall know all about the machine.' He took a step backward, slammed the little door, and turned the key in the lock. I rushed towards it and pulled at the handle, but it was quite secure.

"And then suddenly in the silence I heard a sound which sent my heart into my mouth. He had set the engine at work. The oil lamp still stood upon the floor where I had placed it when examining the floor. By its light I saw that the black ceiling was coming down upon me with a force which would *grind* me to a shapeless *pulp*. I threw myself, screaming, against the door, and dragged with my nails at the lock. I began to think of the least painful position to be in when the press finally made contact. Already I was unable to stand erect, when my eye caught sight of a light through the wooden walls. It was a door. The next instant I threw myself through, and lay half-*fainting* upon the other side. The *panel* had closed again behind me, but the crash of the oil lamp told me how narrow had been my escape.

"I felt a *tugging* at my hand and saw that the woman had come and was urging me onward. I staggered to my feet and ran with her along the corridor and down a winding stair. At the bottom, my guide stopped and looked about her like one who is at her wit's end. Then she threw open a door which led into a bedroom, through the window of which the moon was shining brightly.

"'Quick! Through the window!' she whispered.

"As she spoke a light sprang into view at the further end of the passage, and I saw the lean figure of Colonel Lysander Stark rushing forward with a lantern in one hand and a weapon like a butcher's knife in the other. I rushed across the bedroom, *flung* open the window, and climbed out. I hesitated to jump until I should have heard what passed between my helper and the colonel who pursued me. Before I knew it, however, he was pushing his way past her.

"'Fritz! Fritz!' she cried in English, 'remember your promise after the last time. You said it should not be again. He will be silent! Oh, he will be silent!'

"'You are mad, Elise!' he shouted, struggling to break away from her. You will be the ruin of us. He has seen too much. Let me pass, I say! He dashed her to one side, and rushing to the window, cut at me with his heavy weapon. I had let myself go, and was hanging by the hands to the ledge, when his blow fell. I was conscious of a dull pain, my grip *loosened*, and I fell into the garden below.

"I rushed off among the bushes as hard as I could run, for I understood that I was far from being out of danger yet. Suddenly, however, as I ran, a deadly dizziness and sickness came over me. I glanced down at my hand, which was throbbing painfully, and then, for the first time, saw that my thumb had been cut off and that the blood was pouring from my wound. I *endeavored* to tie my handkerchief round it, but there came a sudden *buzzing* in my ears, and next moment I fell in a dead faint among the rose bushes.

"When I woke up, I jumped to my feet and ran. Much to my surprise, I was near the train station. I took the morning train to London and, upon arriving, went first to have my wound dressed, and then the doctor was kind enough to bring me along here. I put the case into your hands and shall do exactly what you advise."

We both sat in silence for some little time after listening to this extraordinary narrative. Then Sherlock Holmes pulled down from the shelf one of the books in which he placed his cuttings.

"Here is an advertisement which will interest you," said he. It appeared in all the papers about a year ago. Listen to this:

"Lost, on the 9th, Mr. Jeremiah Hayling, aged twenty-six, engineer. Left his lodgings at ten o'clock at night, and has not been heard of since."

"Good heavens!" cried my patient. "Then that explains what the girl said."

"Undoubtedly. Well, every moment now is precious, so if you feel equal to it we shall go down to Scotland Yard at once as a *preliminary* to starting for Eyford."

Some three hours or so afterwards we were all in the train together, bound from Reading to the little Berkshire village. There were Sherlock Holmes, the engineer, Inspector Bradstreet, of Scotland Yard, a plain-clothed officer, and myself. Bradstreet had spread a map of the county out upon the seat and was busy with his *compasses* drawing a circle with Eyford at its center.

"There you are," said he. "That circle is drawn at a *radius* of ten miles from the village. The place we want must be somewhere near that line. You said ten miles, I think, sir. "

"It was an hour's good drive. "

"And you think that they brought you back all that way when you were unconscious?"

"They must have done so. I have a *confused* memory, too, of having been lifted and conveyed somewhere. "

"But why would they have spared you?" I asked.

"I don't know," answered Hatherley.

"Well, I have drawn my circle, and I only wish I knew at what point upon it the folk that we are in search of are to be found. I think South. Few people live there. "

"And I say east," said my patient.

"I am for west," remarked the plain-clothed officer. "There are several quiet little villages up there. "

"And I am for north," said I, "because there are no hills there, and our friend says that he did not notice the carriage go up any. "

"You are all wrong," said Holmes, placing his finger on the center of the circle. "This is where we shall find them. "

"But the twelve-mile drive?" gasped Hatherley.

"Six out and six back. Nothing simpler. You say yourself that the horse was fresh and shiny when you got in. How could it be that if it had gone twelve miles over heavy roads?"

"Indeed. And the nature of this gang?"

"They are coiners on a large scale, and have used the machine to form the metal which has taken the place of silver."

"We have known for some time that a clever gang was at work," said the inspector. "They have been turning out *half-crowns* by the thousand. Thanks to this lucky chance, I think that we have got them right enough."

But the inspector was mistaken, for those criminals were not destined to fall into the hands of justice. As we rolled into Eyford Station we saw a gigantic column of smoke which streamed up from behind a small group of trees.

"A house on fire?" asked Bradstreet as the train steamed off again on its way.

"Yes, sir!" said the *stationmaster*. "Broke out during the night, sir, but it has got worse, and the whole place is in a *blaze*."

"Whose house is it?"

"Dr. Becher's."

"Tell me," broke in the engineer, "is Dr. Becher a German, very thin, with a long, sharp nose?"

The stationmaster laughed heartily. "No, sir, Dr. Becher is a rather heavy Englishman. But he has a gentleman staying with him, a patient, as I understand, who is a foreigner, and he looks as if a little good Berkshire beef would do him no harm."

The stationmaster had not finished his speech before we were all *hastening* in the direction of the fire. Soon we came upon a *whitewashed* house spitting fire from every window.

"That's it!" cried Hatherley, in intense excitement. "There is the gravel drive, and there are the rose bushes where I lay. That second window is the one that I jumped from."

"Well, at least," said Holmes, "you have had your revenge upon them. There can be no question that it was your oil lamp which, when it was crushed in the press, set fire to the wooden walls, though no doubt they were too excited in the chase after you to observe it at the time. Now keep your eyes open in this crowd for your friends of last night, though I very much fear that they are a good hundred miles off by now."

And Holmes's fears came to be realized, for from that day to this no word has ever been heard either of the beautiful woman, the sinister German, or the Englishman. Early that morning a peasant had met a cart containing several people and some very *bulky* boxes driving rapidly in the direction of Reading, but there all traces of the fugitives disappeared, and even Holmes's ingenuity failed ever to discover the least clue as to their whereabouts.

How our engineer had been conveyed from the garden to the spot where he recovered his senses was explained by the discovery of two sets of footprints, one very small and one quite large. He had evidently been carried down by two persons: most probably the silent Englishman and the woman, they both seeming to be of a less violent nature than the German man.

"Well," said our engineer as we took our seats to return once more to London, "it has been a pretty business for me! I have lost my thumb and I have lost a fifty-guinea fee, and what have I gained?"

"Experience," said Holmes, laughing. "Indirectly it may be of value, you know; you have only to put it into words to gain the reputation of being excellent

The Adventure of The Engineer's Thumb

company for the *remainder* of your existence. "

注释

acute [əˈkjuːt] *adj.* 敏锐的

original [əˈridʒənəl] *adj.* 独创的，新颖的

deductive [diˈdʌktiv] *adj.* 演绎的，推论的

consulting [kənˈsʌltiŋ] *adj.* 专门诊视的，咨询的

jerk [dʒəːk] *v.* 猛拉

wrap [ræp] *v.* 包裹，缠绕

agitation [ædʒiˈteiʃən] *n.* 激动，焦虑

inquire [inˈkwaiə] *v.* 询问

monotonous [məˈnɔtənəs] *adj.* 单调乏味的

hysterically [hisˈterikəli] *adv.* 歇斯底里地

hardened [ˈhɑːdənd] *adj.* 坚毅的

despite [disˈpait] *prep.* 不管，尽管

professional [prəˈfeʃənl] *adj.* 专业的，职业的

consultation [kɔnsəlˈteiʃən] *n.* 咨询

outstanding [autˈstændiŋ] *adj.* 突出的，显著的

proficient [prəˈfiʃənt] *adj.* 精通的，熟练的

discreet [disˈkriːt] *adj.* 小心的，慎重的

preserve [priˈzəːv] *v.* 保留，保存

orphan [ˈɔːfən] *n.* 孤儿

reside [riˈzaid] *v.* 居住

restrain [risˈtrein] *v.* 抑制，制止

guinea [ˈgini] *n.* 几尼（英国的旧金币，值一镑一先令）

out of gear 齿轮脱开，失常

awkward [ˈɔːkwəd] *adj.* 尴尬的，不便的

compensate [ˈkɔmpenseit] *v.* 补偿

accommodate [əˈkɔmədeit] *v.* 调节，使适应

deposit [di'pɔzit] *n.* 矿藏,矿床,沉积物

comparatively [kəm'pærətivli] *adv.* 比较地,相当地

compress [kəm'pres] *v.* 压缩

patron ['peitrən,'pæ-] *n.* 主顾

blur [blə:] *n.* 模糊

bumping ['bʌmpiŋ] *n.* 冲震,撞击

fleeting ['fli:tiŋ] *adj.* 短暂的,飞逝的

exterior [eks'tiəriə] *n.* 表面

threshold ['θreʃhəuld] *n.* 门口

slam [slæm] *v.* 砰地关上

faintly ['feintli] *adv.* 模糊地,朦胧地

chill [tʃil] *n.* 寒战

hinder ['hində] *v.* 阻碍

obstacle ['ɔbstəkl] *n.* 障碍,妨害物

wearisome ['wiərisʌm] *adj.* 使疲倦的,乏味的

despairing [dis'pɛəriŋ] *adj.* 绝望的,失望的

chamber ['tʃeimbə] *n.* 室,房间

piston ['pistən] *n.* 活塞

stiffness ['stifnis] *n.* 坚硬,费劲

gigantic [dʒai'gæntik] *adj.* 巨大的

lever ['li:və] *n.* 控制杆

reenter [,ri:'entə] *v.* 再进入

inadequate [in'ædikwit] *adj.* 不适当的

stoop [stu:p] *v.* 弯腰

mutter ['mʌtə] *v.* 咕哝,嘀咕

grind [graind] *v.* 碾(碎)

pulp [pʌlp] *n.* 浆状物

fainting ['feintiŋ] *n.* 昏晕,不省人事

panel ['pænl] *n.* 面板,嵌板

tugging ['tʌgiŋ] *n.* 牵引感

The Adventure of The Engineer's Thumb

fling [fliːŋ] *v.* 猛推

loosen ['luːsn] *v.* 松开,放松

endeavor [in'devə] *v.* 努力,尽力

buzz [bʌz] *v.* 嗡嗡作响

preliminary [pri'liminəri] *n.* 预备(行为或措施)

compass ['kʌmpəs] *n.* 圆规

radius ['reidiəs] *n.* 范围,半径

confused [kən'fiuːzd] *adj.* 混乱的

half-crown 半克朗(英国银币名,值二先令六便士)

stationmaster ['steiʃ(ə)nmɑːstə(r)] *n.* 站长

blaze [bleiz] *n.* 火焰

hasten ['heisn] *v.* 加速,赶紧

whitewash ['hwaitwəʃ] *v.* 用石灰水刷白

bulky ['bʌlki] *adj.* 体积大的

remainder [ri'meində] *n.* 剩余部分

THE ADVENTURE OF SHOSCOMBE OLD PLACE

Upon entering Sherlock Holmes's study, I found him bent over a low-power microscope. He ignored my presence a short while and then straightened himself up, saying *triumphantly*: "It is glue, Watson. Unquestionably it is glue."

"Is it one of your cases?" I asked.

"No; my friend, Merivale, of the Yard, asked me to look into the case." He looked *impatiently* at his watch. "I had a new client calling, but he is overdue. By the way, Watson, you know something of racing?"

"I ought to. I pay for it with about half my wound pension."

"Then what about Sir Robert Norberton? Does the name recall anything?"

"Well, I should say so. He lives at Shoscombe Old Place, and I know it well, for my summer quarters were down there once. I remember hearing of him horsewhipping a *moneylender* once. He nearly killed the man."

"Ah, he sounds interesting! Does he often *in-*

dulge in that way?"

"Well, he has the name of being a dangerous man. He is about the bravest rider in England — second in the Grand National a few years back."

"Capital, Watson! Now, can you give me some idea of Shoscombe Old Place?"

"Well, the famous horse training quarters are to be found there. And they *breed* dogs... *spaniels*, I believe. They're the pride of the lady of Shoscombe Old Place."

"And the head horse trainer," said Holmes, "is John Mason. This is a letter from him which I am unfolding. Is the lady of Old Shoscombe Place Sir Robert's wife?"

"No. He lives with his *widowed* sister, Lady Beatrice Falder. Shoscombe Old Place belonged to her late husband. Meantime, she draws the rents every year."

"And brother Robert, I suppose, spends the said rents?"

"That is about the size of it. He is a devil of a fellow and must lead her a most uneasy life. Yet I have heard that she is devoted to him. But what is wrong at Shoscombe?"

"Ah, that is just what I want to know. And here, I expect, is the man who can tell us."

The door had opened and the page had shown in a tall, clean-shaven man with the firm, austere expression which is only seen upon those who have to control horses or boys. He bowed with cold self-possession and seated himself upon the chair to which Holmes had waved him.

"You got my note, Mr. Holmes?"

"Yes, Mr. Mason, but it explained nothing."

"Well, then let me begin by saying that I think that my employer, Sir Robert, has gone mad."

"Why do you say so?"

"Well, sir, I believe Shoscombe Prince and the Derby have turned his brain."

"That is a horse you are running?"

"Best in England, Mr. Holmes. Sir Robert has got to win this Derby. He's up to the neck, and it's his last chance. He thinks of nothing but the horse and the race. His whole life is on it. He's holding off the money collectors till then. If the Prince fails him, he is done."

"It seems a rather *desperate gamble*, but where does the madness come in?"

"I don't believe he sleeps at night. He is down at the *stables at* all hours. His eyes are wild. It has all been too much for his nerves. Then there is his conduct to Lady Beatrice! They have always been the best of friends. And she loved the horses as much as he did. Every day at the same hour she would drive down to see them — and, above all, she loved the Prince. But now she seems to have lost all interest in the horses. For a week she has driven past the stables with never so much as 'Good-morning!'"

"You think there has been a quarrel?"

"And a bitter quarrel at that. Why else would he give away her pet dog that she loved as if he were her child? He gave it a few days ago to old Barnes, who keeps the Green Dragon, three miles off."

"That certainly did seem strange."

"Of course, with her weak heart and illness one couldn't expect that she could get about with him, but he spent two hours every evening in her room. Now he never goes near her. And she takes it to heart. She is drinking, Mr. Holmes — drinking like a fish. It's all changed, Mr. Holmes, and there is something *damned rotten* about it. But then, again, what is master doing down at the old church tomb at night? And who is the man that meets him there?"

Holmes rubbed his hands.

"Go on, Mr. Mason. You get more and more interesting. "

"It was the servant who saw him go. Twelve
o'clock at night and raining hard. So next night I was
up at the house and, sure enough, master was off
again. Stephens and I went after him. He went
straight to the old ruined *chapel* in the park. It's a
dark, damp, lonely place by day, but there are few in
that county that would have the nerve to go near it at
night. But master's not afraid. He never feared anything in his life. But what is he doing there in the
night time?"

"Wait a bit!" said Holmes. "You say there is another man there. "

"That's right, but it's no one I know. I saw him
from rather close that night, for the moon was quite
bright. By his face, he seems a mean dog, I should
say. What could he have in common with Sir Robert?"

Holmes sat for some time lost in thought.

"Who keeps Lady Beatrice Falder company?" he
asked at last.

"There is her maid, Carrie Evans. She has been with her five years. But she seems more devoted to Sir Robert than to the lady... if you know what I mean."

"I quite understand, Mr. Mason. Don't you think the quarrel between brother and sister may lie there?"

"Well, the scandal has been pretty clear for a long time."

"But she may not have seen it before. Let us suppose that she has suddenly found it out. She waits to get rid of the woman. Her brother will not permit it. The *invalid*, with her weak heart and inability to get about, has no means of enforcing her will. The lady refuses to speak, and takes to drink. Sir Robert in his anger takes her pet dog away from her. Does not all this hang together?"

"Well, it might do — so far as it goes."

"Exactly! But how do the visits to the old tomb fit into things?"

"And there is something more that I can't fit in. Why should Sir Robert want to dig up a dead body?"

Holmes sat up *abruptly*.

"We only found it out yesterday — after I had

written to you. Yesterday Sir Robert had gone to London, so Stephens and I went down to the tomb. It was all in order, sir, except that in one corner was a bit of a human body. "

"You say Sir Robert was away yesterday. Has he returned?"

"We expect him back today. "

"When did Sir Robert give away his sister's dog?"

"It was just a week ago. "

Holmes sat for some time in silent thought.

"I am not clear yet what you want me to do in this matter, Mr. Mason," he said at last. "Can't you make it more definite?"

"Perhaps this will make it more definite, Mr. Holmes," said our visitor.

He took a paper from his pocket, and *unwrapping* it carefully, he exposed a burned *fragment* of bone.

"Where did you get it?" asked Holmes.

"There is a central heating *furnace* in the cellar under Lady Beatrice's room. It's been off for some time, but Sir Robert *complained* of cold and had it on again, one of my friends runs it. This very morning he came to me with this, which he found in the ashes. He didn't like the look of it."

"Nor do I," said Holmes. "What do you make of it, Watson?"

"It's definitely human," I replied.

"Exactly!" Holmes had become very serious. "You say that Sir Robert was not at home last night?"

"No, sir."

"Then, whoever was burning bones, it was not he. Tell me, is there good fishing in that part of Berkshire?"

"Well, sir, I suppose so."

"Good. Watson and I are famous fishermen — are we not, Watson? We'll go to the Green Dragon tonight."

Thus it was that on a bright May evening Holmes and I found ourselves alone in a first-class carriage. We finally arrived at an old-fashioned tavern, where a sporting host, Josiah Barnes, entered eagerly into our plans for fishing.

"What about the Hall Lake?" said Holmes.

The face of the innkeeper clouded.

"That wouldn't do, sir. That's too near to Sir

Robert's training ground. He doesn't *tolerate* people being near it. "

"We'll stay away then, Mr. Barnes. By the way, that was a most beautiful dog that was in the hall. "

"I should say it was. That was the real Shoscombe breed. "

"Now, if it is a fair question, what would a prize dog like that cost?"

"More than I could pay, sir. It was Sir Robert himself who gave me this one. That's why I have to keep it on a lead. It would be off to the Hall in a no time if I gave it its head. "

When the landlord had left us, Holmes said to me: "Sir Robert is still in London, I hear. We might, perhaps, enter the tomb tomorrow night, for there are one or two points on which I should like *reassurance*. "

"Have you any theory, Holmes?"

"Only this, Watson, that something happened a week or so ago which has cut deep into the life of the household. Let us consider. Sir Robert is mad keen upon winning the Derby. He is in the hands of the money collectors, and may at any moment be sold up and his racing stables seized by his creditors. He is a daring and desperate man. He derives his income from his sister. His sister's maid is his willing tool."

"But the tomb?"

"Ah, yes, the tomb! Let us suppose, Watson, that Sir Robert has done away with his sister."

"My dear Holmes, it is out of the question."

"Sir Robert is a man of an honorable *stock*. But you do occasionally find a *crow* among the eagles. Let us for a moment argue upon this supposition. He could not fly the country until he had realized his fortune by winning the race. Therefore, he has still to stand his ground. To do this he would have to *dispose* of the body of his victim, and he would also have to find a *substitute* who would pretend to be her. The woman's body might be conveyed to the tomb, which is a place so seldom visited, and it might be secretly destroyed at night in the furnace, leaving behind it such evidence as we have already seen. What say you to that, Watson?"

"Well, it is all possible. . . ."

"I think that there is a small experiment which we may try tomorrow, Watson, in order to throw some light on the matter."

The next day, at about eleven o'clock, we started for a walk, and Holmes obtained leave to take the black Shoscombe dog with us.

"This is the place," said he as we came to two high park gates. "About midday, Mr. Barnes informs me, the old lady takes a drive. When it comes through the gates I want you, Watson, to stop the coachman with some question. Never mind me. I shall be busy with something else."

Within a quarter of an hour we saw the carriage coming down the long avenue. Holmes crouched behind his bush with the dog. I stood unconcernedly swinging a *cane* in the roadway. As it came through the gate, I noticed an attractive lady inside, sitting next to an elderly person, wrapped heavily in clothes. I held up my hand with an *authoritative* gesture, and as the coachman pulled up I inquired if Sir Robert was at home.

At the same moment Holmes stepped out and *released* the dog. With a joyous cry it dashed forward to the carriage and sprang upon the step. Then in a moment its eager greeting changed to *furious rage*, and it snapped at the black skirt above it.

"Drive on! Drive on!" shrieked a harsh voice.

The coachman *lashed* the horses, and we were left standing in the roadway.

"Well, Watson, the dog thought it was his mistress, but he found it was a stranger. Dogs don't make mistakes."

"But it was the voice of a man!" I cried.

"Exactly! Now, let's go fishing a while, in order to keep up appearances."

Later that evening, we met Mr. John Mason at the park gates.

"Good evening, gentlemen," said he. "I got your note, Mr. Holmes. Sir Robert is expected to return tonight."

"Alright. You can show us the tomb and then be back in time for his arrival."

It was pitch-dark and without a moon, but Mason led us over the grasslands until a dark mass *loomed* up in front of us which proved to be the ancient chapel. We entered the tomb and, lighting our lantern, *illuminated* the sad place. Inside were piles of *coffins*, some of lead and some of stone, extending upon one side right up to the roof which lost itself in the shadows above our heads.

"You spoke of some bones, Mr. Mason. Could

you show them before you go?"

"They are here in this corner." The trainer strode across and then stood in silent surprise as our light was turned upon the place. "They are gone," said he.

"So I expected," said Holmes, chuckling. "I fancy the ashes of them might even now be found in that *oven* which had already consumed a part. It may mean a long search, and we need not *detain* you. I fancy that we shall get our solution before morning."

When John Mason had left us, Holmes set to work making a very careful examination of the graves. It was an hour or more before Holmes came to a box standing on end before the entrance to the vault. I heard his little cry of satisfaction and was aware from his hurried but purposeful movements that he had reached a goal. He drew from his pocket a short box-opener and set to work. There was a tearing sound as the lid gave way, but it had hardly hinged back and partly revealed the contents before we had an unforeseen interruption.

Someone was walking in the chapel above. It was the firm, rapid step of one who came with a definite purpose and knew well the ground upon which he walked. A light streamed down the stairs, and an instant later the man who bore it was *framed* in the *entranceway*. He was a terrible figure, huge in *stature* and fierce in manner, with a heavily mustached face and angry eyes.

"Who the devil are you?" he thundered. "And what are you doing upon my property?"

Holmes advanced to meet him.

"I also have a question to ask you, Sir Robert," he said in his sternest tone. "Who is this? And what is it doing here?"

He turned and tore open the lid behind him. In the glare of the lantern I saw a body wrapped in a sheet from head to foot.

Sir Robert staggered back with a cry and supported himself against a stone tomb.

"Who are you?" he cried.

"My name is Sherlock Holmes," said my companion. "Possibly it is familiar to you. In any case, it seems to me that you have much to answer for."

Sir Robert glared for a moment.

"Appearances are against me, I'll admit, but I could act no otherwise."

"I should be happy that you think so, but I fear

your explanations must be before the police. "

Sir Robert shrugged his broad shoulders.

"Well, if it must be, it must. Come up to the house and you can judge for yourself how the matter stands. "

A quarter of an hour later we found ourselves in the *gunroom* of the old house. It was comfortably furnished, and here Sir Robert left us for a few moments. When he returned he had two companions with him; the one, the young woman whom we had seen in the carriage; the other, a small rat-faced man. These two wore an appearance of utter *bewilderment*, which showed that Sir Robert had not yet had time to explain to them the turn events had taken.

"There," said Sir Robert with a wave of his hand, "are Mr. and Mrs. Norlett. Mrs. Norlett, under her *maiden* name of Evans, has for some years been my sister's *confidential* maid. I have brought them here because I feel that my best course is to explain the true position to you, and they are the two people upon earth who can back up what I say. Now, Mr. Holmes, listen to a plain statement of the facts.

"You must know that I am running a dark horse

for the Derby and that everything depends upon my success. If I win, all is easy. If I lose — well, I dare not think of that!"

"I understand the position," said Holmes.

"I am dependent upon my sister, Lady Beatrice, for everything. I am deeply in the hands of the money collectors. I have always known that if my sister were to die my creditors would come to claim her property. I would lose everything. Well, Mr. Holmes, my sister died just a week ago."

"And you told no one!"

"What could I do? Absolute ruin faced me. If I could keep things quiet for three weeks all would be well. Her maid's husband — this man here — is an actor. I've asked him to disguise himself as my sister. Anyway, my sister died of the illness which had long *afflicted* her."

"Well, what did you do?"

"The body could not remain there. On the first night Norlett and I carried it out to the old well house, which is now never used. We were followed, however, by her pet dog, which cried continually at the door, so I felt some safer place was needed. I got rid of the dog, and we carried the body to the tomb of the church. There was no *indignity* or irreverence, Mr. Holmes. It seemed to me that it would be no *unworthy* resting place if we put her for the time in one of the tombs of her husband's ancestors lying in what is still holy ground. We opened such a tomb, removed the contents, and placed her as you have seen her. We then burned the old bones in the central furnace. There is my story, Mr. Holmes."

Holmes sat for some time lost in thought.

"There is one *flaw* in your narrative, Sir Robert," he said at last. "Your *bets* on the race, and therefore your hopes for the future, would hold good even if your creditors seized your estate."

"The horse would be part of the estate. What do they care for my bets? As likely as not they would not run him at all."

"Well, Sir Robert," said Holmes, rising, "this matter must, of course, be referred to the police. It was my duty to bring the facts to light, and there I must leave it. As to the *morality* or *decency* of your conduct, it is not for me to express an opinion. It is nearly midnight, Watson, and I think we may make our way back to the inn."

It is generally known now that this singular episode ended upon a happier note than Sir Robert's actions deserved. Shoscombe Prince did win the Derby, the sporting owner did net eighty thousand pounds in bets, and the creditors did hold their hand until the race was over, when they were paid in full, and enough was left to *reestablish* Sir Robert in a fair position in life. The police took a lenient view, and, beyond a mild *criticism* for the delay in registering the lady's death, the lucky owner got away without harm from this strange incident in a career which has now outlived its shadows and promises to end in an honored old age.

注释

triumphantly [traiˈʌmfəntli] *adv.* 成功地,耀武扬威地

impatiently [imˈpeiʃəntli] *adv.* 不耐烦地

moneylender [ˈmʌnilendə(r)] *n.* (尤指经营典当的) 放债者

indulge [inˈdʌldʒ] *v.* 纵情,沉溺

breed [briːd] *v.* 饲养,使繁殖

spaniel [ˈspænjəl] *n.* 狗的一种,西班牙猎狗

widow [ˈwidəu] *vt.* 使成寡妇

desperate [ˈdespərit] *adj.* 不顾一切的,拼死的

gamble [ˈgæmbl] *n.* 赌博,投机

stable [ˈsteibl] *n.* 马厩

damned [dæmd] *adv.* 非常

rotten [ˈrɔtn] *adj.* 恶劣的,坏的

chapel ['tʃæpəl] *n.* 小教堂

invalid [in'vælid] *adj.* 有病的

abruptly [ə'brʌptli] *adv.* 突然地

unwrap [ʌn'ræp] *v.* 打开,展开

fragment ['frægmənt] *n.* 碎片

furnace ['fə:nis] *n.* 炉子,熔炉

complain [kəm'plein] *v.* 抱怨

tolerate ['tɔləreit] *v.* 容忍

reassurance [,ri:ə'ʃuərəns] *n.* 放心

stock [stɔk] *n.* 血统

crow [krəu] *n.* 乌鸦

dispose [dis'pəuz] *v.* 处置,处理掉

substitute ['sʌbstitju:t] *n.* 代替者,替代品

cane [kein] *n.* 手杖

authoritative [ɔ:'θɔritətiv] *adj.* 命令的

release [ri'li:s] *v.* 释放

furious ['fjuəriəs] *adj.* 狂怒的,激烈的

harsh [hɑ:ʃ] *adj.* 粗糙的,刺耳的

lash [læʃ] *v.* 鞭打

loom ['lu:m] *v.* 隐现,迫近

illuminate [i'lju:mineit] *v.* 照亮

coffin ['kɔfin] *n.* 棺材

oven ['ʌvən] *n.* 炉灶

detain [di'tein] *v.* 延迟,耽搁

frame [freim] *v.* 塑造,构出

entranceway ['entrəns,wei] *n.* 入口

stature ['stætʃə] *n.* 身材

stern [stə:n] *adj.* 严厉的

gunroom [gʌnru:m] *n.* (住宅中的)猎枪室

bewilderment [bi'wildəmənt] *n.* 困惑,慌张

The Adventure of Shoscombe Old Place

maiden [ˈmeidn] *adj.* 未婚的

confidential [kɔnfiˈdenʃəl] *adj.* 心腹的

afflict [əˈflikt] *v.* 使痛苦，折磨

indignity [inˈdigniti] *n.* 侮辱（的行为）

unworthy [ʌnˈwəːði] *adj.* 不足取的

flaw [flɔː] *n.* 漏洞，缺点

bet [ˈbet] *n.* 赌注

morality [məˈræliti] *n.* 道德

decency [ˈdiːsnsi] *n.* 面子

reestablish [ˌriːisˈtæbliʃ] *v.* 重建

criticism [ˈkritisiz(ə)m] *n.* 批评

推 荐 书 目

书 名 简 介	定价
一、儿童床头灯英语学习读本：	
床头灯儿童英语语音(1 书,16 开,彩印,CD、音带、MP3 任一种) 　　根据儿童发音的特点,对48 个音标进行了简单、明了的讲解。图文并茂。录音清晰、缓慢、饱满,对容易混淆的音,凸现差别。	30.00/套 （估）
床头灯幼儿英文词典(1 书,16 开,彩印,CD、音带、MP3 任一种) 　　选择了66 个儿童最常用的英文单词,图文并茂。录音清晰、缓慢、标准、地道,便于孩子模仿。配有优美的音乐,有助于孩子高效记忆。此书是儿童学英语的启蒙书,为孩子学习《床头灯儿童英文故事》等作了铺垫。	23.00/套
床头灯儿童英文词典(1 书,16 开,彩印,1MP3) 　　全书选择了1300 多个儿童常用的英文单词,所配例句十分有趣、生动。图文并茂。录音清晰、缓慢、标准、地道,配有优美的音乐,便于孩子高效记忆。	38.00/套
床头灯儿童英文短剧(1 书,16 开,彩印,附 DVD 1 张) 　　本书是英语语音标准的外国孩子和中国孩子拍摄的教学片。语言简洁、地道,语音标准,内容富有童趣,便于模仿。这样可以使您的孩子和剧中的孩子很快地靠近,相对容易地走进剧中,走进英语世界。	30.00/套
床头灯儿童英文故事 1—10(每集书 1 本,彩印,附录音音带、CD、MP3任一种) 　　语言简洁、地道、实用,语音（童声）标准、漂亮,内容有趣(英美孩子都熟悉的内容)、积极向上,配以优美的音乐和富有童趣的画面,使孩子具有身临其境的感受,是极好的儿童学英语的入门书。	28.00/辑
最好的儿童英文故事—爸爸和我(音带版)(1 书,16 开,彩印,1 音带) 　　英汉双语录音,语音标准、清晰漂亮。语言地道、实用,内容有趣(英美孩子都熟悉的内容)、积极向上,配以优美的音乐和富有童趣的画面,使孩子具有身临其境的感受。也可以用它学汉语。	16.00/套
最好的儿童英文故事—爸爸和我(CD 版)(1 书,16 开,彩印,1CD)	16.00/套
最好的儿童英文故事—兔山(音带版)(1 书,16 开,彩印,1 音带)	15.00/套

书 名 简 介	定价
最好的儿童英文故事—兔山(CD 版)(1 书,16 开,彩印,1CD)	16.00/套
最好的儿童英文故事—猫咪凯蒂和小老鼠(音带版)(1 书,16 开,彩印,1 音带)	15.00/套
最好的儿童英文故事—猫咪凯蒂和小老鼠(CD 版)(1 书,16 开,彩印,1CD)	16.00/套
最好的儿童英文故事—又来了一只狗(音带版)(1 书,16 开,彩印,1 音带)	15.00/套
最好的儿童英文故事—又来了一只狗(CD 版)(1 书,16 开,彩印,1CD)	16.00/套
最好的儿童英文故事—动物和数字(音带版)(1 书,16 开,彩印,1 音带)	15.00/套
最好的儿童英文故事—动物和数字(CD 版)(1 书,16 开,彩印,1CD)	16.00/套
最好的儿童英文歌曲(一)(书 1 本,大 32 开,附录音音带、CD、MP3 任一种) 　　美国教育家丹尼斯夫妇主编。本书选用原汁原味、几乎每个美国儿童都熟悉的英文歌曲,英文地道、标准、现代。歌词译文准确,讲解到位。所配录音在每首原声歌曲后,配以纯正、清晰的英文歌词朗诵,便于学习。使用后你肯定也会认为它确实是最好的儿童英文歌曲。	25.00/套
最好的儿童英文歌曲(二)(附录音音带、MP3 任一种)	22.00/套
正音——美语发音基本功(书 1 本,CD、音带、MP3 任一种) 　　一针见血地指出了中国人说英语的习惯性错误,采用针对中国人的矫治训练。中式发音→美式发音。	26.00
简单老外——英语急用现学 10 天口语(书 1 本,音带 2 盒) 　　由美国教育家丹尼斯夫妇为中国人写的口语书,语音地道、优美,语言标准、实用,是美国人天天讲的英语。由美国播音员和演员在美国录制。	36.00/套
简单老外——英语急用现学 10 天口语(书 1 本,CD 2 张)	38.00/套
标准美国英语口语—怎样用英语进行深入交谈(音带版)(1 书 4 带) 　　丹尼斯夫妇主编。帮你解决怎样用英语进行深入交谈的问题。配有高品质录音。	32.00/套
美国英语口语—怎样用英语进行深入交谈(CD 版)(1 书 4 CD)	36.00/套

书 名 简 介	定价
中学生床头灯英语学习读本(初、高中) 　　本读物由美国作家执笔,用流畅的现代英语写成。语言标准、地道,内容适合中学生,难度与中学课本同步。录音语音标准、地道、清晰、漂亮,是通向英语自由境界的基石。	
初一:	
爱丽丝梦游仙境(1 书 1MP3)	15.80/估
格林童话(1 书 1MP3)	15.80/估
小飞侠(1 书 1MP3)	15.80/估
天方夜谭(1 书 1MP3)	15.80/估
鲁滨逊漂流记(1 书 1MP3)	15.80/估
热爱生命(1 书 1MP3)	15.80/估
初二:	
辛巴达历险记(1 书 1MP3)	16.80/估
汤姆·索亚历险记(1 书 1MP3)	16.80/估
丛林历险记(1 书 1MP3)	16.80/估
金银岛(1 书 1MP3)	16.80/估
绿野仙踪(1 书 1MP3)	16.80/估
杨柳风(1 书 1MP3)	16.80/估
初三:	
雾都孤儿(1 书 1MP3)	17.80/估
秘密花园(1 书 1MP3)	17.80/估
圣诞欢歌(1 书 1MP3)	17.80/估
不可不知的科学家的成长历程(1 书 1MP3)	17.80/估
哈克贝利·费恩历险记(1 书 1MP3)	17.80/估

书 名 简 介	定价
地心游记(1 书 1MP3)	17.80/估
高一:	
圣经故事(1 书 1MP3)	18.80/估
爱伦·坡短篇小说选(1 书 1MP3)	18.80/估
星球大战(1 书 1MP3)	18.80/估
堂吉诃德(1 书 1MP3)	18.80/估
福尔摩斯探案集(1 书 1MP3)	18.80/估
不可不知的发明家的故事(1 书 1MP3)	18.80/估
高二:	
呼啸山庄(1 书 1MP3)	19.80/估
罗马故事(1 书 1MP3)	19.80/估
希腊神话故事(1 书 1MP3)	19.80/估
拿破仑的故事(1 书 1MP3)	19.80/估
三个火枪手(1 书 1MP3)	19.80/估
奥德赛(1 书 1MP3)	19.80/估
3000 词《床头灯英语学习读本》 　　本套读物均由美国作家执笔,以流畅的现代英语,用 3300 个最常用的英语单词写成。语言标准、地道。通俗易懂,对于难于理解之处,均有注释。全系列 100 种,已出 50 种,分成纯英文版和英汉对照版两种形式。每种书别配有高质量的音带(2-4 盒)和 MP3(1 张)。有很多读者说这是他们自己读完的第一本英语小说(以前读其它英文小说一般读几页就因为生词太多而无法读下去,不得不放弃),是通向英语自由境界的基石。	英汉对照 10 元/本; 纯英文版 8 元/本; MP3 8 元/张 音带每盒 5 元; 1 书 1MP3 18 元
①《查泰莱夫人的情人》(音带 4 盒)	20.00

书 名 简 介	定价
②《飘》(音带 4 盒)	20.00
③《红与黑》(音带 4 盒)	20.00
④《了不起的盖茨比》(音带 3 盒)	15.00
⑤《歌剧魅影》(音带 2 盒)	10.00
⑥《三个火枪手》(音带 4 盒)	20.00
⑦《傲慢与偏见》(音带 3 盒)	15.00
⑧《呼啸山庄》(音带 3 盒)	15.00
⑨《简·爱》(音带 4 盒)	20.00
⑩《儿子与情人》(音带 3 盒)	15.00
3000 词床头灯英语学习读本 Ⅱ：	
⑪《鲁滨逊漂流记》(音带 3 盒)	15.00
⑫《大战火星人》(音带 4 盒)	20.00
⑬《巴斯克维尔猎犬》(音带 3 盒)	15.00
⑭《时间机器》(音带 3 盒)	15.00
⑮《远大前程》(音带 3 盒)	15.00
⑯《彼得·潘》(音带 3 盒)	15.00
⑰《格列佛游记》(音带 3 盒)	15.00
⑱《黑骏马》(音带 3 盒)	15.00
⑱《黑骏马》(1 MP3)	8.00
⑲《汤姆·索亚历险记》(音带 4 盒)	20.00
⑳《杨柳风》(音带 3 盒)	15.00

书　名　简　介	定价
3000 词床头灯英语学习读本Ⅲ：	
㉑《德伯家的苔丝》(音带 3 盒)	15.00
㉒《化身博士》(音带 3 盒)	15.00
㉓《野性的呼唤》(音带 3 盒)	15.00
㉔《阿丽思漫游奇境记》(音带 4 盒)	20.00
㉕《弗兰肯斯坦》(音带 2 盒)	10.00
㉖《白鲸》(音带 3 盒)	15.00
㉗《环游地球 80 天》(音带 4 盒)	20.00
㉘《圣诞欢歌》(音带 4 盒)	20.00
㉙《圣经故事》(音带 4 盒)	20.00
㉚《希腊神话故事》(音带 4 盒)	20.00
3000 词床头灯英语学习读本Ⅳ：	
㉛《红字》(音带 4 盒)	20.00
㉜《永别了武器》(音带 4 盒)	20.00
㉝《摩尔·弗兰德斯》(音带 3 盒)	15.00
㉞《密探》(音带 4 盒)	20.00
㉟《包法利夫人》(音带 4 盒)	20.00
㊱《觉醒》(音带 4 盒)	20.00
㊲《爱玛》(音带 4 盒)	20.00
㊳《维尔德费尔庄园的主人》(音带 4 盒)	20.00
㊴《霍华德庄园》(音带 4 盒)	20.00

书 名 简 介	定价
⑩《卡斯特桥市长》(音带4盒)	20.00
3000 词床头灯英语学习读本 V：	
④《吸血鬼》(音带4盒)	20.00
④《螺丝在拧紧》(音带4盒)	20.00
④《秘密花园》(音带3盒)	15.00
④《少年维特的烦恼》(音带4盒)	20.00
④《地心游记》(音带4盒)	20.00
④《小妇人》(音带4盒)	20.00
④《海底两万里》(音带4盒)	20.00
④《白牙》(音带4盒)	20.00
④《理智与情感》(音带4盒)	20.00
⑩《莎士比亚戏剧故事》(音带4盒)	20.00
5000 词《床头灯英语学习读本》 由美国作家用 5500 词写成,最大限度地保留了原著的语言特色,而且难度适中,很适合具有 4000 词左右的词汇量又读不懂原著的读者阅读,是读懂原著的阶梯。全系列 57 种,有纯英文和英汉对照两种形式。	
①《查泰莱夫人的情人》(英汉对照)	15.80
①《查泰莱夫人的情人》(纯英文)	13.80
②《三个火枪手》(英汉对照)	17.80
②《三个火枪手》(纯英文)	14.80
③《歌剧魅影》(英汉对照)	16.80
③《歌剧魅影》(纯英文)	13.80
④《高老头》(英汉对照)	14.80
④《高老头》(纯英文)	14.80

书 名 简 介	定价
⑤《吸血鬼》(英汉对照)	16.80
⑤《吸血鬼》(纯英文)	14.80
⑥《红与黑》(英汉对照)	16.80
⑥《红与黑》(纯英文)	15.80
⑦《包法利夫人》(英汉对照)	16.80
⑧《奥德赛》(英汉对照)	13.80
⑧《奥德赛》(纯英文)	13.80
⑨《傲慢与偏见》(英汉对照)	18.80
⑨《傲慢与偏见》(纯英文)	16.80
⑩《福尔摩斯探案集》(英汉对照)	15.80
⑩《福尔摩斯探案集》(纯英文)	14.80
⑪《飘》(英汉对照)	16.80
⑪《飘》(纯英文)	13.80
⑫《红字》(英汉对照)	14.80
⑫《红字》(纯英文)	13.80
⑬《圣经故事》(英汉对照)	16.80
⑬《圣经故事》(纯英文)	14.80
⑭《理智与情感》(英汉对照)	16.80
⑭《理智与情感》(纯英文)	14.80
⑮《约翰·克里斯朵夫》(英汉对照)	14.80
⑯《呼啸山庄》(英汉对照)	16.80

书 名 简 介	定 价
⑯《呼啸山庄》(纯英文)	14.80
⑰《汤姆·索亚历险记》(英汉对照)	16.80
⑰《汤姆·索亚历险记》(纯英文)	13.80
⑱《堂吉珂德》(英汉对照)	15.80
⑱《堂吉珂德》(纯英文)	14.80
⑲《弗兰肯斯坦》(英汉对照)	15.80
⑳《华胜顿广场》(英汉对照)	17.80
⑳《华胜顿广场》(纯英文)	14.80
㉑《名利场》(英汉对照)	16.80
㉒《环游地球八十天》(英汉对照)	16.80
㉒《环游地球八十天》(纯英文)	13.80
㉓《巴黎圣母院》(英汉对照)	17.80
㉓《巴黎圣母院》(纯英文)	14.80
㉔《三十九级台阶》(英汉对照)	13.80
㉔《三十九级台阶》(纯英文)	14.80
㉕《伊利亚特》(英汉对照)	14.80
㉖《简·爱》(英汉对照)	16.80
㉖《简·爱》(纯英文)	14.80
㉗《儿子与情人》(英汉对照)	16.80
㉗《儿子与情人》(纯英文)	14.80
㉘《鲁滨逊漂流记》(英汉对照)	14.80

书 名 简 介	定价
㉘《鲁滨逊漂流记》(纯英文)	13.80
㉙《悲惨世界》(英汉对照)	16.80
㉙《悲惨世界》(纯英文)	15.80
㉚《纯真年代》(英汉对照)	15.80
㉛《德伯家的苔丝》(英汉对照)	16.80
㉜《伟大的英国女人》(英汉对照)	14.80
㉝《莎士比亚戏剧故事集》(英汉对照)	17.80
㉝《莎士比亚戏剧故事集》(纯英文)	16.80
㉞《小妇人》(英汉对照)	16.80
㉞《小妇人》(纯英文)	15.80
㉟《十日谈》(英汉对照)	15.80
㉟《十日谈》(纯英文)	14.80
㊱《夜色温柔》(英汉对照)	15.80
㊲《天方夜谭》(英汉对照)	15.80
㊲《天方夜谭》(纯英文)	13.80
㊳《白衣女人》(英汉对照)	16.80
㊴《清教徒的故事》(英汉对照)	16.80
㊵《成吉思汗》(英汉对照)	14.80
㊵《成吉思汗》(纯英文)	14.80
㊶《希腊神话》(英汉对照)	16.80
㊶《希腊神话》(纯英文)	15.80

书 名 简 介	定价
㊷《闹鬼的旅馆》(英汉对照)	23.80
㊷《闹鬼的旅馆》(纯英文)	14.80
㊸《罗马故事》(英汉对照)	14.80
㊸《罗马故事》(纯英文)	15.80
㊹《了不起的盖茨比》(英汉对照)	15.80
㊹《了不起的盖茨比》(纯英文)	14.80
㊺《亚历山大大帝》(英汉对照)	17.80
㊺《亚历山大大帝》(纯英文)	16.80
㊻《彼得大帝》(英汉对照)	19.80
㊼《基督山伯爵》(英汉对照)	16.80
㊼《基督山伯爵》(纯英文)	15.80
㊽《四个伟大的美国人》(英汉对照)	18.80
㊾《恋爱中的女人》(英汉对照)	16.80
㊿《丛林历险记》(英汉对照)	15.80
51《埃及艳后》(英汉对照)	20.80
52《征服者威廉》(英汉对照)	18.80
53《恺撒》(英汉对照)	17.80
54《查理一世》(英汉对照)	16.80
55《红玫瑰皇后——玛格丽特安茹》(英汉对照)	19.80
56《耶路撒冷的末日》(英汉对照)	13.80
57《维多利亚女王》(英汉对照)	19.80

书　名　简　介	定价
(57)《维多利亚女王》(纯英文)	16.80
6500 词《床头灯英语学习读本》 由美国作家用 6500 词写成,最大限度地保留了原著的语言特色,而且难度适中,很适合具有 6000 词左右的词汇量又读不懂原著的读者阅读,是读懂原著的阶梯。全系列 20 种,有纯英文和英汉对照两种形式。	
①《查理二世》(英汉对照)	19.80
②《小公主》(英汉对照)	22.80
③《本杰明·富兰克林自传》(英汉对照)	20.80
④《海盗》(英汉对照)	22.80
⑤《不可不知的波斯战争故事》(英汉对照)	21.80
⑥《不可不知的德国历史故事》(英汉对照)	22.80
⑦《不可不知的日本历史故事》(英汉对照)	21.80
⑧《不可不知的美国历史故事》(英汉对照)	21.80
⑨《伊索寓言》(英汉对照)(1 书 1MP3)	20.80
⑩《娜娜》(英汉对照)	15.80
⑪《不可不知的法国历史故事》(英汉对照)	20.80
⑫《不可不知的欧洲历史故事》(英汉对照)	23.80
⑬《不可不知的发明家的故事》(英汉对照)	17.80
⑭《森林的秘密》(英汉对照)	14.80
⑮《嗜血的尼禄》(英汉对照)	19.80
⑯《不可不背的美丽英文》(英汉对照)(1 书 1MP3)	25.80
⑰《伊丽莎白女王》(英汉对照)	19.80

书 名 简 介	定价
⑱《不可不知的科学家的成长历程》(英汉对照)	16.80
⑲《你能用英文读懂的美国历史》(英汉对照)	49.80
⑳《亚瑟王》(英汉对照)	19.80/估
考试虫英文电影课堂: 　　通过英文原版电影学英语无疑是学英语的最好方法,但很多人弄不懂电影对白,本系列讲解部分不放过任何一个疑难之处,帮你彻底看懂电影。	
音乐之声(音带版)(1 书 2 带)	22.00
音乐之声(CD 版)(1 书 2CD)	24.00
罗马假日(音带版)(1 书 2 带)	22.00
罗马假日(CD 版)(1 书 2CD)	24.00
简·爱(音带版)(1 书 2 带)	22.00
简·爱(CD 版)(1 书 2CD)	24.00
人鬼情未了(音带版)(1 书 2 带)	22.00
人鬼情未了(CD 版)(1 书 2CD)	24.00
魂断蓝桥(音带版)(1 书 2 带)	22.00
魂断蓝桥(CD 版)(1 书 2CD)	24.00
飘(音带版)(1 书 2 带)	22.00
飘(CD 版)(1 书 2CD)	24.00
狮子王(音带版)(1 书 2 带)	22.00
狮子王(CD 版)(1 书 2CD)	24.00

全国各大外文、新华、民营书店均有售。

销售咨询电话:010－64815618/15　64815606　82863351/52

北京零售地址：①朝阳区慧新西街 33 号院底商航空书店　　电话：64978486
　　　　　　　②海淀西大街 36 号海淀图书城昊海楼 108 汉英达书刊发行
　　　　　　　有限公司　　电话：62534432
邮购地址：①北京安外小关东里 14 号航空书店（收）　　　100029
　　　　　　电话：64978486
　　　　　②北京市海淀区中关村东路华清商务会馆 1501 室　王润阁（收）
　　　　　　100083　　电话：010－82863351　82867367
邮购书免邮费，音带加收 5 元邮资（包装费）
售后服务电话：010－64815606　64815618　13601274554　13601002700
E-mail：wrx1@ vip. sina. com
孩子学英语的 Blog：http：//blog. sina. com. cn/kaoshichong
床头灯英语的 Blog：http：//blog. sina. com. cn/chuangtoudeng
网　　址：http：//www. yinghanda. com

床头灯系列反馈意见调研表

请将下面的问卷填好后寄至：北京市海淀区中关村东路华清商务会馆 1501 室（100083）王润霞（收）；上网 www.sinoexam.com 或在地址栏里输入"考试虫"回车即可进入网站（网络实名）；或 E—mail 至 wrx1@vip.sina.com.

书名：_____ （请勿忘填写书名）

1．您的个人资料：

姓名 _____ 性别 _____ 年龄 _____ 职业 _____

通信地址 _____ 省 _____ 市 _____ 邮编 _____

E-mail _____ 电话 _____ 其它 _____

2．本书吸引您的原因：

☐品牌 ☐书名 ☐作者 ☐内容有益 ☐编校质量 ☐版式设计 ☐封面设计
☐印装质量 ☐所配音像制品的质量 ☐促销活动或赠品 ☐网上服务
☐其它 _____

3．您认为本书的不足之处是：

☐封面设计 ☐印刷 ☐纸张 ☐字体 ☐内文编辑 ☐内容
☐其它 _____

4．您的建议： _____
_____
_____
_____

5．您通常以何种方式购书：

☐书店 ☐网上书店 ☐团购 ☐亲友推荐 ☐销售人员推荐
☐其它 _____

6．您如何得知本书消息：

☐逛书店 ☐书讯 ☐广告 ☐图书馆 ☐书展 ☐亲友介绍
☐老师介绍 ☐网络 ☐其它 _____

您的中肯建议，将得到特别奖励。

床头灯系列简介

好的英语是读出来的。床头灯系列能使你真正轻松愉快地学好英语。

1. 系统性：

床头灯系列	儿童	语　音	
		故　事	（10集）（已出版）
		短　剧	1种　　（已出版）
		对　话	（2本）（已出版）
		歌　曲	（2集）（已出版）
		童　谣	（已出版）
		词　典	（2本）（已出1本）
	初、高中	初一～高二英汉对照和纯英文版各6种,共30种	
	3000词	英汉对照50本　（已出版）	
		纯英文版50本　（已出版）	
	5000词	英汉对照57本　（已出版）	
		纯英文版57本	
	6500词	英汉对照20本	
		纯英文版20本	

2. 科学性：

它凝聚了大批国内外一流英语教育专家的科研、实践成果。

3. 趣味和高雅并存：

每个故事都经过精心挑选，它不但能使你读下去、爱不释手，而且顺便能学到英美文化，提高自身修养。

4. 素质教育与考试：

本体系完全属于素质教育，但真正使用本体系进行学习的人考分都很高，原因是他（她）们真会了。使用本体系的目的旨在帮助读者能用英语生活、工作，而不仅仅是考试。

5. 配有高品质录音：

从儿童至3000词系列均配有录音。